MW00534371

EXPLORING ART OF THE ANCIENT AMERICAS

THE JOHN BOURNE COLLECTION

EXPLORING ART OF THE ANCIENT AMERICAS

THE JOHN BOURNE COLLECTION

DORIE REENTS-BUDET

Contributions by
Julie Lauffenburger, Jessica Arista,
Glenn Gates, and Marc Zender

With an introduction by John Bourne

Photography by Susan Tobin

THE ART WALTERS MUSEUM g

The Walters Art Museum, Baltimore
in association with D Giles Limited, London

PUBLICATION OF THIS CATALOGUE HAS BEEN
GENEROUSLY SUPPORTED BY A GIFT FROM JOHN BOURNE.

© 2012 The Trustees of the Walters Art Gallery, Baltimore
The Walters Art Museum
600 North Charles Street
Baltimore, Maryland 21201
http://thewalters.org

First published in 2012 by GILES
An imprint of D Giles Limited
4 Crescent Stables
139 Upper Richmond Road
London, SW15 2TN, UK
www.gilesltd.com

ISBN (hardback): 978-1-907804-05-2
ISBN (paperback): 978-0-911886-76-4

Library of Congress Cataloging-in-Publication Data

Walters Art Museum (Baltimore, Md.)
  Exploring art of the ancient Americas : the John Bourne collection /
Dorie Reents-Budet ; contributions by Julie Lauffenburger ... [et al.] ;
with an introduction by John Bourne.
     p. cm.
  Includes bibliographical references and index.
  ISBN 978-1-907804-05-2 (hardcover) -- ISBN 978-0-911886-76-4 (pbk.)
  1. Indian art--Central America--Exhibitions. 2. Indian
art--Mexico--Exhibitions. 3. Indian art--South America--Exhibitions. 4.
Indians of Central America--Antiquities--Exhibitions. 5. Indians of
Mexico--Antiquities--Exhibitions. 6. Indians of South
America--Antiquities--Exhibitions. 7. Bourne, John (John G.)--Art
collections--Exhibitions. 8. Art--Private
collections--Maryland--Baltimore--Exhibitions. 9. Walters Art Museum
(Baltimore, Md.)--Exhibitions. I. Reents-Budet, Dorie. II.
Lauffenburger, Julie A. III. Title.
  F1434.2.A7W35 2012
  704.03'970728--dc23
              2011040167

All measurements are in centimeters;
height precedes width precedes depth.

For the Walters Art Museum:
Manager of Curatorial Publications: Charles Dibble
Curatorial Publications Coordinator: Jennifer Corr
Designed by Jennifer Corr

For D Giles Limited:
Copy-edited and proof-read by Sarah Kane
Indexed by Sue Farr
Produced by GILES, an imprint of D Giles Limited, London
Printed and bound in Hong Kong

Front cover illustration: Seated Male Figure with Incense
Burner (detail), TL.2009.20.222 (no. 27)
Spine illustration: Maskette Pendant, TL.2009.20.231 (no. 8)
Back cover illustration: Human Effigy Pendant, TL.2009.20.74 (no. 103)
Frontispiece: Effigy Bottle (detail), 2009.20.37 (no. 128)

Unless otherwise noted, catalogue entries are by Dorie Reents-Budet.
Authorship of other contributions, including the technical commentaries,
is indicated parenthetically in the entries as follows:
    JA   Jessica Arista
    BF   Briana Feston
    JL   Julie Lauffenburger
    MZ   Marc Zender

CONTENTS

FOREWORD

John Bourne and Chac, ca. 1947

I met John Bourne and had the privilege of visiting his magnificent home and collection in 2000, during one of my many visits to Santa Fe as guest of longtime friends, Walters supporters, and collectors Julianne and George Alderman; it happened to be on the occasion of John's seventy-fifth birthday celebration. I was struck not only by the range and quality of John's collection of the arts of the ancient Americas, but also by the overall aesthetic of his home, where a strikingly abstract West Mexican terracotta of a seated woman might be juxtaposed with a thoroughly naturalistic Colonial painting of the Virgin and Child, both within just a few feet of a dramatic African mask and one of John's own canvases, which at first might be taken for a Hans Hoffman. But my most vivid memory from that initial visit is of John himself, whom I found to be a gifted story-teller with a charmingly playful sense of humor. I will never forget his vivid account of his seemingly accidental discovery—in 1946, at age nineteen, with Carl Frey—of the great Mayan ruins at Bonampak, in the jungles of Chiapas, and of his sometimes comical adventures along the way with the Lacandon Indians, who until then had experienced little contact with the modern world. Happily, we are able to reprint John's compelling narrative of these events in the present volume.

The arts of the ancient Americas have long had an especially powerful attraction for me, mostly, I think, because I had experienced over ten years the joy of nearly daily engagement with the spectacular collection of ancient American art assembled by Robert and Mildred Bliss at Dumbarton Oaks in Washington, D.C., where I was, until coming to the Walters, Associate for Byzantine Art Studies. I was also keenly aware, when I met John in 2000, of Henry Walters' early fascination with the arts of the ancient Americas; indeed, a hundred years before, Henry was busily acquiring small gold figures and animals at Tiffany's, just a few blocks south of his New York residence. And there was a further connection between John and the Walters that I learned of only years later; namely, that Henry Walters and John's grandfather, who was the president of the Singer Sewing Machine Company, were both members of the New York Yacht Club at the time that Henry was beginning his own small collection of the arts of the ancient Americas. Certainly, the two were acquainted, and perhaps they even discussed Henry's new, exotic collecting interest.

My sole hope at the time of that first meeting with John Bourne was that someday he might be willing to lend the Walters a few works from his collection. Of course, I could

Zacatecas figurines (cat. no. 68 and checklist no. 50) among Colonial paintings and sculpture in John Bourne's Santa Fe, New Mexico, residence, 2001.

not then have dreamed that a decade later John's long friendship with Juli and George Alderman would blossom into the spectacular gift that is the subject of this publication and its accompanying exhibition. Without question, this gift marks one of the great milestones in the seventy-year history of the Walters; now, for the first time, our visitors may experience works of art reflective of the great civilizations of the Western Hemisphere, complementing those of the Mediterranean and European artistic traditions that have been at the core of this museum's offerings since it opened in 1934. In addition, John's extraordinary bequest of $4 million for the research, conservation, display, and teaching of the arts of the ancient Americas—which follows upon an endowment gift of $3.25 million in 2009 from the Ziff family of New York City with a similar focus—means that in the decades to come the Walters will be at the forefront nationally in exploring and bringing to the public's attention the rich cultural history of our own hemisphere, from ancient Peru to pre-Conquest Mexico. For all of this we owe an immense debt of gratitude to John Bourne, and also to Juli and George Alderman, without whom this would never have happened.

This catalogue and accompanying exhibition were realized in a remarkably short time through the scholarship and seemingly boundless energy of guest curator Dr. Dorie Reents-Budet. Dorie worked in close and constant collaboration not only with John, Juli, and George, but also with Walters Senior Conservator Julie Lauffenburger and Assistant Conservator Jessica Arista, both of whom made John's collection not only their professional focus, but also their passion. And finally, special thanks are due to Walters Publications Manager Charles Dibble and to designer Jennifer Corr, who together brought this beautiful publication together on the tightest of deadlines.

Gary Vikan
Director, The Walters Art Museum

Burial Urn, cat. no. 94

RECOLLECTIONS OF MY EARLY TRAVELS IN CHIAPAS

DISCOVERIES AT OXLAHUNTUN (EL PERRO),
MIGUEL ANGEL FERNANDEZ, BONAMPAK, AND LACANHÁ

JOHN BOURNE

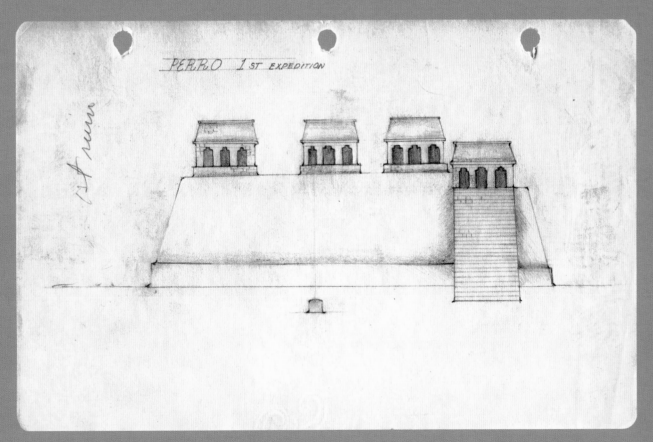

Reconstruction of Oxlahuntun site. Drawn on site by John Bourne

There have been many different stories about events that happened on the expeditions of 1945 and 1946 in the Lacanhá jungles of Chiapas, Mexico. The following account is an attempt to set the record straight.

J.B., DECEMBER 2000, SANTA FE, NEW MEXICO[1]

I first met Giles Healey in Los Angeles. My mother's cousin had introduced us, and we met at my mother's home sometime in mid-September 1945. I recently had been discharged from the Army, and Healey had come to Los Angeles to see one of his backers, Kenneth Macgowan. Healey was completing a photographic assignment, "The Maya through the Ages," for the United Fruit Company, and Macgowan had just finished producing the feature film *Lifeboat*, starring Tallulah Bankhead, the year before.

Macgowan learned of my interest in the Maya from either Healey or Dr. Frederick Hodge, the Director of the Southwest Museum in Los Angeles, and telephoned to invite me to lunch at the studio commissary. During lunch, Macgowan told me about Healey's recent explorations in the jungles of southern Mexico. It seems that Healey had heard about some newly discovered ruins from *chicleros*, itinerant workers who tap the chicle tree for sap, a substance that's processed and made into chewing gum. The chicleros had been working in the Lacanhá region, and Healey was going back to Mexico to photograph the find.

Macgowan wanted to know how I had become interested in the Maya, and I told him that when I was in high school I had been captivated by a documentary film and lecture that had been presented by Dana and Ginger Lamb about their travels in the jungles of Chiapas. After reading their book, *Enchanted Vagabonds*, I picked up as many books on the subject of the Maya as I could find, and from that time on I was forever hooked.

After touring the Paramount lot, Macgowan asked me if I would like to join Healey when he returned to Mexico. I knew Healey wasn't too happy about having a nineteen-year-old kid tag along, but Macgowan had taken a liking to me, so to please his mentor, Healey included me. At the time it never occurred to me that Healey would put me to work as his lackey.

In October Healey headed back to San Cristóbal, where he lived with his wife, Sheila, their baby girl, CeCe, and his mother. Because I had to wrap up several loose ends before I could leave, I was unable to join him just then; however, a few weeks later I was on a Mexicana flight to Mexico City. The following day I flew to Oaxaca and then to Tuxtla Gutierrez, the capital of Chiapas. In the capital city I slept in a top-floor room of a slummy hotel in the center of town. Although the room was enormous, it had only a bed and two old crates that served as bedside tables. Because the room had no roof, a canvas tarp had been stretched wall-to-wall to keep out the rain.

The next morning I ran into the owner of the hotel. When he asked me where I was going, I said I was headed into the jungles of Chiapas to live with a group of Lacandon Indians. He appeared shocked and told me he had just met some travelers who had recently returned from there. They had reported to him that the Lacandon were still cannibals. Of course I told him this was nonsense, but he vigorously pleaded with me to reconsider my plans to visit these "savages."

After breakfast I hitched a ride on a weathered, mud-caked station-wagon bus leaving for San Cristóbal. It was

1. For those who wish to read the unedited version of *Recollections of My Early Travels in Chiapas*, go to www.mesoweb.com and look under "publications" for monograph.

crammed with Mexicans, rope-tied baggage, and open-weave baskets filled to the brim with squawking chickens. The trip, which took all day, was hot, dusty, and anything but fun. A few kilometers from town the paved section of the as-yet-unfinished Pan-American highway ran out and turned into a rutty dirt road. After a while, we started climbing a narrow road into the cool, pine-covered high country. A couple of times we had to stop to fix flat tires, and another time we had to get out to clear away some rocks blocking the road.

By late afternoon, as we were nearing our destination, I noticed small groups of drunken Indians weaving back and forth across the road on their way home from the markets of San Cristóbal.

Healey and his family were renting a small Colonial house (Número 10 Calle José María Santiago) within walking distance of the center of town. It had a small neglected inner courtyard and tiny windowless rooms with doors opening onto a U-shaped portal. A door at the north end of the house led to a walled-in vacant lot and a wooden outhouse that we all used. In one of the rooms of the house Healey had set up his photographic studio. Against one wall of his darkroom was a large, empty, dugout canoe. When I asked about it, Healey said he filled it with water and used it to wash his prints. He also told me that it substituted for a bathtub, but I never saw it put to that use. He and his family rarely bathed.

Daybreak in San Cristóbal always began with the crowing of roosters, followed by the mournful rings of cracked bells, the hiss and blasts of skyrockets (an Indian mix of Catholic and pagan ritual to celebrate a new day), and other irritating sounds coming from the more than twenty churches spread across town. The unnerving morning clamor lasted until sunup. After breakfast I would gather my bedding and hang it on a line stretched across the courtyard. Then, using a flit gun, I'd douse the sheets with insecticide, hoping to kill the fleas. The house was always crawling with them. Somehow they got mixed in with the fresh pine needles the Indians brought us each week to carpet our rooms and kitchen. Unfortunately, my spray-soaked bed linen had a small checkered pattern that made it almost impossible to locate any flea that escaped the spray of the flit gun, and so I got little sleep because I had to spend a good part of the night chasing down fleas with a flashlight.

Healey's mother was a short, bony French woman with quaint peasant traits. When Healey was around she spoke only French. Her English was limited, but it was good enough to ask me to help her with a chore I really detested. At least once a week she would call me to the kitchen and hand me a live chicken, which I had to hold over a bowl while she cut its neck and let the warm blood drain. After the last drop of blood was spent she'd pick up the bowl, hurry across the courtyard to her grandchild's room, and give the warm blood to the baby. After watching the baby drool blood from the corners of her mouth I decided to give CeCe the nickname "The Vampire Baby."

San Cristóbal, once the seat of power for all of Central America, was well off the beaten track and, by 1945, an almost forgotten city. It had few vehicles and no banks. To cash a traveler's check I had to go to the hardware store where, tucked into a dark corner, was a tiny safe stuffed with pesos. Telephone service was even worse. For a city of a few thousand people, there was only one telephone in town. The phone was in a government building on the main plaza, and direct calls could be made only to the capital of Chiapas. If you needed to call any other place, an operator in Tuxtla Gutierrez had to listen to your message and then relay it to its final destination.

Healey told me a black woman who had modeled for some of Diego Rivera's paintings came to the town a couple of years before. When Healey took her to the main plaza to visit the Indian market, they were suddenly surrounded by a group of frightened Indians who picked up rocks and began pelting the terrified African woman. She finally was able to escape into a building unscathed, unaware that the Indians were convinced she must be some kind of black devil.

While I explored the city and got my supplies together, Healey began packing equipment: some nonperishable foods, mosquito nets, hammocks, rubberized ponchos, and such essentials as medicines and toilet paper that we would take

Refueling plane before takeoff

El Cedro airstrip

Airstrip "terminal"

with us on our trip. I had been there three weeks when we finally were ready to leave. Healey telephoned a friend of his in Tuxtla Gutierrez and arranged to charter his plane for our trip. It turned out to be a handsome vintage Ford Tri-motor built in the early '30s. We hired one of the town's scarce trucks to take us and our gear to a large cemetery that adjoined a pasture on the outskirts of town. There we watched our pilot dive-bomb the field to chase off a group of agitated cows before landing. Once he landed and taxied over to the truck, we loaded our gear, then got in and took off and circled the town before flying south, barely clearing the jungle canopy. We were headed to Ocozingo to pick up Carl Frey. Carl, who was thirty, had been in the Lacanhá area with Franz Blom in 1943, and Healey was planning to use Carl's familiarity with the region to his advantage. An hour later we landed in Ocozingo and I met Carl, who later became a close friend.

A neighbor of Carl's had lent him a portion of his finca, a ranch called El Real. Carl had stocked it with chickens and pigs and also had set aside a few acres for growing corn and loofah, a dried fibrous vegetable sponge that he said the Navy used to filter oil in submarines during World War II. Carl despised the war and hated the United States, especially his hometown of Staunton, Illinois. He told me he preferred living in the jungle rather than register for the draft. Sometime in July 1945 Carl had taken a wife, a fifteen-year-old illiterate mestiza named Caralampia Solis.

The one night we spent in Ocozingo could have been a scene taken straight from a Wild West movie. The pool-hall bar was loud and rowdy. We were sound asleep in the early hours of the morning when gun shots rang out, followed by the distant cries of the wounded man repeatedly screaming for a doctor.

The next morning, Carl's wife came to watch our plane take off for Tenosique, Tabasco, a frontier town on the Usamacinta River, and the center of chicle and mahogany operations. After landing there, we transferred our gear to a small, single-engine plane for the one hour flight to El Cedro. There were no seats, and we had to sit on the floor next to a pile of crates. The outer skin of the plane had a large rip that flapped in the wind, and through it I caught glimpses of the jungle treetops below. The plane began to drop abruptly, gliding along a steep path and landing on a short, grassy runway that had been hacked out of raw jungle. At one end of the airstrip was a small, open, thatched hut with a windsock attached to a pole stuck in the roof. We had arrived at El Cedro's airstrip "terminal." The sky was cloudless that day, but the ground had been thoroughly soaked from a recent *Norte*, a steady, almost endless drizzle.

It was early November when we reached El Cedro, a chicle camp named after the Cedro River, which ran alongside. There were four thatched huts in the camp. The largest hut was used as operations headquarters and contained a

Under the porch of the chicle headquarters

Chiclero's hut

small office and one large room that had five canvas beds strapped to four posts that were stuck in the dirt. The kitchen was housed in a much smaller hut that had a doorless entrance and a small, eye-level window. A wood dining table, six chairs, and a large, doublebottomed cauldron completed the kitchen furnishings. The unlidded cauldron sat on the floor and was filled with drinking water brought up from the muddy Cedro River. Normally these containers were used only for cooking raw chicle. The two remaining huts were used by the families of chicleros. From them we learned about some chicle gatherers who were fugitives from justice and said to be avoiding capture by the police by hiding in isolated chicle camps deep within the nearby jungle.

In the middle of the dining-room table sat an old rusty can filled with damp sugar. The first one to reach for a clean spoonful had to stir the sugar and then wait while an army of roaches spilled over the sides and disappeared under the table. Every night a few rats would fall from the thatched kitchen ceiling into our clouded water supply, and each morning the cook would toss the drowned rats out the door by their tails, but their hair and droppings always polluted our drinking water.

The day after our arrival was overcast and light rains fell: another *Norte* had arrived. A few Lacandon Indians had wandered into camp, some holding banana leaf "umbrellas" over their heads. They had come with food to trade for goods, mainly for shotgun shells, although they still relied on bows and arrows when ammunition was not available.

While we waited for the weather to clear, Healey spent most of the time cleaning his two movie cameras. His one treasured piece of equipment was a fancy 16mm Eastman Kodak movie camera he kept in a carefully wiped black leather case. His backup was a less costly Swiss-made Bolex. One day I watched him empty a jar of silica gel desiccant into a pan and heat it over a fire to drive off the moisture. After the crystals turned from pink to cobalt blue, they were cooled and then packed with his cameras and film to keep the equipment from being damaged by the humidity, which averaged 95 percent.

The next day our mules were loaded, and we prepared to leave for the first ruin we planned to explore. We poled a small dugout across the Cedro River and were supposed to be followed by five or six pack mules, guided by two *arrieros*, mule drivers. However, our mules were swept downstream by the strong current and landed on a muddy bank some distance away. Luckily we were able to catch up with them and found our equipment still intact. Because of the constant rains, the trail was a quagmire, with an endless series of two-foot-deep trenches filled with pools of soupy muck. Every hoof beat dug the trenches even deeper and splattered us with globs of sticky mud. To stay dry we hurriedly put on our ponchos, and just in time; the rains started again, and the showers pelted us for the rest of the day.

We arrived late in the evening at Ruin Number 1, unloaded our gear and fed the mules with leaves cut from the Ramón tree. After we put up our hammocks and mosquito nets, we rain-proofed our makeshift enclosures with rubberized ponchos. We were careful to keep our toes away from the netting so vampire bats wouldn't bite our toes and infect us with rabies or some other nasty disease.

The next morning we found that vampire bats had attacked three of our mules; their open wounds were still oozing red. Long after the bats had left for the caves and vaulted rooms in Maya temples that were their homes, the anticoagulant they had injected into our mules had still not worn off. Eventually two mules succumbed from the nightly bat attacks.

This was the morning I discovered that Healey expected me to carry his equipment around as we explored. Only later, during some free time, was I able to take my sketch pad and draw elevations and floor plans of the ruins, after using a tape to measure the buildings. Healey was annoyed, claiming he could get all the measurements we needed from his photographs of the ruin he named El Perro after he saw what he believed to be the figure of a dog carved in the plastered doorpost of one building. Later, El Perro was renamed Oxlahuntun.

That night, after we had gone to bed, I was awakened by a sudden, eerie silence; all jungle sounds had abruptly stopped. Seconds later I heard a splintering noise followed by the crashing sound of a large tree knocking down the forest as it fell. It was pitch black and I held my breath in fear, having no idea where the tree trunk would land. Then, finally, I heard it hit some distance away. It was several minutes later before the sounds of the jungle fully returned to their normal pitch.

Early the next morning we packed our mules and headed for Ruin Number 2, which later was renamed Miguel Angel Fernandez by Healey in honor of the renowned Mexican archaeologist. We traveled for hours through the rain forest without a bite to eat, but Healey, unaware that I suffered from hypoglycemia, was angry with me for stopping to untie a bag for food. I think it was on this leg of the journey that bad feelings started between Carl and Healey, when Carl heard him say, "To get ahead in this world, you have to use people like rungs in a ladder."

During our preliminary exploration of this large site, in one temple we found twelve "god" pots, which Healey said we would divide among us. "God" pots are small bowls with the face of an idol attached to the rim and were used for burning copal incense. Later that afternoon I took one of them back to camp to examine it. Carl came over and warned me to be careful to keep it out of sight. Not only did he feel that the Lacandon would be upset if they saw the god pot had been removed from the temple, but also that Healey would have a fit if he knew I had taken it. I didn't want to cause any trouble, so I wrapped it in a towel and put it in my duffel bag.

After locating Ruin Number 3, which Healey named the Bee Ruin, we headed back to El Cedro. (I didn't go with them to this ruin because I was running a high fever at the time and stayed in my hammock all day.)

When we got back to the chicle camp the next day, Carl overheard Healey talking to the *jefe*, the boss of the chicle camp. He wanted a letter typed and sent out on the next plane. Healey dictated a letter in Spanish in which he bragged about how he alone had found three important Maya ruins in the Lacanhá area. In his letter he said he would mail photographs of the ruins to the proper authorities when he returned to San Cristóbal.

Carl was furious and rushed to tell me how Healey was taking all the credit. Carl said he had a plan to make sure we received credit where credit was due. Believing there were still

plenty of ruins waiting to be discovered, he wanted me to fly to Mexico City, buy a camera and film, and come back with him to El Cedro. We'd meet in Mexico City after Christmas and later return to comb this area of the jungle to look for more ruins. The three of us were all preparing to leave soon, but I was really excited and started to plan my departure immediately. It was already late December, and I told Healey that when I got back to Mexico City I would be staying at the Hotel Montejo, on the Paseo de la Reforma, where he could ship the belongings I had stored with him in San Cristóbal. I told him that after I received my things I would be returning to the United States.

I had stayed at the Hotel Montejo while in Mexico City, on my way to San Cristóbal, and I went back there because it was small, informal and popular with many of the archaeologists who came down from the States. I hadn't bathed in weeks, and so, before I did anything else, I took a long shower—after soaking in the tub. After a quick nap I got dressed and went down to the hotel restaurant for my first civilized meal in months. After dinner, gorged and ready for a much-deserved rest, I finally went to bed.

I was awakened in the middle of the night by a tickling sensation in my throat. I jumped out of bed, rushed to the bathroom and coughed up a handful of long, squirming, pink worms. I was scared stiff. Knowing that only one drugstore in town was required to stay open all night, I dressed as fast as possible, flew out the door, flagged down a taxi, and yelled for the driver to take me there. The pharmacist laughed hysterically when I told him what had happened. He gave me some pills and told me that I would be fine by morning, and I was. I never did find out what kind of worms I had, but they looked like the common garden variety.

As planned, I located a first-class German camera, a 35mm Contax with a built-in light meter. I also bought twenty-five rolls of Super XX black-and-white film. It was just after the war, and color stock was unavailable. In addition to photographing the Lacandon, Carl and I had also talked about recording their chants and flute music. In 1945 tape recorders hadn't yet reached the market; however, I was fortunate to locate a machine called a SoundScriber that was about the size of a standard typewriter and one step up from a Dictaphone. I paid 1,000 pesos for it, then about $80 U.S. When the SoundScriber was hooked to a microphone and turned on, a needle cut a groove in a five-inch, green plastic disk, and a pick-up arm played back the recording. There was only one problem: because the SoundScriber operated on alternating current, I had to buy a generator that ran on gasoline because El Cedro had no electricity. I finally found one, for $64 U.S., that would generate enough electricity to power the recording machine. It was too dangerous to carry around a highly flammable liquid, so I decided to wait until we got to Tenosique, which would be our last chance to buy gasoline. I added almost 500 feet of electric cord, an assortment of plugs, sockets, and one light bulb. Our plan was to hang the 100-watt light bulb over the jefe's desk at El Cedro and turn it on one hour a night for two or three nights. This was to be our small token of appreciation for his assistance and was

limited only by our need to conserve the fuel we needed to make the recordings.

In late December my mother came down from California for a one-week visit. At one point during her stay, I put her to work stringing glass beads as gifts for the Lacandon women. I couldn't remember if any of them had ever seen a mirror, so I picked up a bunch of small, round ones from a sidewalk vendor to take with me when I delivered the gifts.

In mid-January the hotel desk clerk handed me an envelope; it was a letter from Healey, dated January 7, 1946. He agreed to ship my things, but only if I sent his hammock back, along with Photostat copies of all the drawings and measurements I had made of the first two ruins. I wired back to tell him that his hammock had been cleaned and mailed weeks ago. I didn't know what had happened; perhaps it had been lost or stolen. I remembered he had told me he could get all the measurements of the buildings from the photographs he

Launch anchored on the banks of the Grijalva River

had taken and promised to mail to me. I never got them, so, since he clearly had no intention of keeping his part of the bargain, I decided not to send him Photostats of my drawings.

Carl arrived Sunday, January 13, and we went to the flea market to look for a Victrola, hoping to bribe the Lacandon to show us some more ruins. We found an old wind-up phonograph with two bottom doors that opened to let out the sound. We also picked up a few extra needles and a stack of 78-rpm records, including jazz, a few operas, and one or two platters of ranchero music.

A week later we flew to Villahermosa, the capital of Tabasco. It was a filthy, humid city with open sewage ditches running down the middle of the dirt roads. We found a hotel next to the river front and stayed in the city for three or four days while we waited to book passage on a launch going to Tenosique.

Our boat left a few days later and moved slowly down the muddy Grijalva, passing rich farmlands. Near the stern was an open galley where a Mexican with drooping paunch prepared our meals. At night hammocks were strung shoulder-to-shoulder across the deck. When we arrived in the gulf port of Frontera the next day, we found the estuary cluttered with floating stalks of bananas drifting out to sea. They had been thrown into the river, too ripe to be shipped.

As we headed up the Usamacinta River, passing fertile grasslands and banana plantations, clusters of overgrown Maya temple mounds appeared at almost every turn. There were many delays along the way because, among his other duties, our pilot had to visit friends and deliver the mail.

When we finally docked in Tenosique, we stayed overnight in a ramshackle hotel on the only road that went straight through town. The next day we filled two 10-gallon tins with gasoline and caught a plane back to El Cedro, arriving on January 31. The chicleros, and a few Lacandon who were lined up along the grass runway seemed happy to see us.

While we were gone, Healey had hired a muleteer to remove all the "god" pots from the second ruin and put them in a box tagged with his name. After paying the arriero for bringing them back to El Cedro, Carl told the jefe the three of us had agreed to split the twelve pots between us, and he immediately gave us permission to open the carton. Instead of Healey getting all twelve, we each ended up with four pots. Carl wanted the rare and important drum pot. Because there was only one of these, I agreed he should have it.

Leaving El Cedro, we walked two hours to one of the Lacandon caribals, a cluster of thatched huts. Carl told me that the word caribal derives from "Caribe," the name the Lacandon call themselves. There were only five of these caribals in this part of the Lacanhá region, with a total combined population of twenty-five: eight males and seventeen females.

We made our home at the caribal of patriarch ChanKin, who lived with his mother; his two wives, NaBor and NahaKin;

Hammocks strung across the covered deck

Street scene in Tenosique

ChanKin

ChanBor

two sisters, and three children. ChanBor and his two wives lived in a hut close by. Because of the redundancy of Lacandon names, the chicleros had given Spanish names to the Indians with whom they had the most contact. They named ChanKin, Obregón, and called ChanBor, José Pépe.

We had found a book with pictures of another Lacandon group in a bookstore in Mexico City and brought it with us. We showed ChanBor and ChanKin the photographs of a Lacandon man and woman wearing native Lacandon coltons, a kind of long serape with closed sides. Having never seen a photograph before, they had not learned how to "read" them, something they share with a number of other, nonliterate tribes. They carefully studied the images, first turning them upside down, then sideways, then flipping them over. I suppose the subtle contrasts of light and shadow were confusing to them. Laughing, they quickly became bored, gave up, and walked away with puzzled looks on their faces.

ChanKin's house was by far the largest hut in the caribal, with a tall, A-shaped entrance. The sides and back of

his hut wore skirts of palm thatch that almost touched the ground. Several woven native hammocks were strung along the perimeter of the room, tied to posts that held up the rafters. A covered clay jug filled with water stood next to the hearth. Beans, corn, and rice were kept in lidded clay pots, and cooked meat hung in nets draped over the wood beams to keep it out of the reach of dogs and *jabelinas*, wild boars that somehow had been domesticated and had become the Lacandon's favorite pet.

Looking around I saw what looked like human body parts dangling from nets hanging from the rafters. Stunned, I looked closer and discovered they were only the arms and legs of roasted monkeys with all traces of hair singed off. Now I understood why the owner of the hotel in Tuxtla Gutierrez thought the Lacandon were cannibals.

Each day began with the wives making tortillas. These were not the ordinary round variety we are accustomed to but large, square ones. Carl said he thought the masa must have been ground of fermented corn because the cooked tortillas

Bor weaing a colton and carrying a jaguar purse

NaBor, one of Bor's wives

tasted like sourdough bread. Unlike our daily ritual, the Lacandon don't eat three meals a day but nibble on food all the time.

Considering that they didn't have soap, the Lacandon were amazingly clean. Every day they would bathe in a stream, scrubbing their bodies with coarse sand; however, this practice didn't rid them of lice. I often saw them sitting on the ground, one behind the other, chattering in Maya while parting hair and catching lice, which they promptly gobbled down. I suppose they copied this behavior from watching monkeys preen themselves.

One day two Lacandon women came over to my hammock and started parting my hair, looking for lice. They were baffled when they couldn't find any and broke into laughter. They then proceeded to pull back my shirt sleeves exposing the hair on my arms. Giggling with delight, they said I must

be a relative of some funny kind of monkey. Unlike Europeans, the Lacandon have no body hair except for eyebrows, eyelashes, and the thick black hair on their heads.

Their babies are born with a purple spot at the end of the spine that varies from the size of a saucer to a half-dollar. The spot usually fades away by the time they reach eleven. Someone told me this discoloration, which looks like a bruise, is known as a Mongolian spot because it is commonly found on children from that part of Asia. A few Lacandon have a fold in the upper eyelid, called the epicanthic fold, a feature that is also found in Asia.

The Lacandon were terrified of catching a cold. If they heard someone cough or sneeze, they fled into the jungle for days, sometimes abandoning their caribal for good in an attempt to escape death. They had never built up an

Lacandon girl with epicanthic fold

Carranza (Kayom)

immunity to the cold or flu viruses, and, as a result, usually developed pneumonia after catching a cold. While we were at El Cedro, the Lacandon called Carranza had contracted pneumonia and was dying. Fearing the worst, his mother, her legs crippled by disease, had literally dragged herself along a trail from a distant caribal to be at his side. The next day the plane arrived with some vials of penicillin, and the camp "doctor" was able to save his life.

Because the Lacandon were delighted with all the trinkets we gave them, each of us got a "wife" to enjoy during our stay. Unfortunately, my wife, NaBor, gave me an unwelcome gift, and I had to have a series of shots to rid myself of gonorrhea. The camp had run out of penicillin, so we sent to Tenosique for another batch of penicillin and treated all of the Lacandon who showed signs of the disease.

NaBor and I slept side-by-side, in a large native hammock, her feet by my face and mine next to hers. Before going to bed she would go over every inch of the hammock and eat any fleas she caught, and when the nights were cold she

would keep a fire going underneath our hammock. Some of the Lacandon customs seemed odd to us. They would sneak off to bury their nail clippings and strands of cut hair, afraid that someone might use them to cast an evil spell. Although they never talked about their religious beliefs and kept the place where they performed their rituals a secret, ChanBor confessed that the most important god they worshiped was called Nohoch Zac Yum. A chiclero who spoke Yucatec Maya told us it meant Great White Father.

Most of the chicleros looked down on the Lacandon because they were polygamous, traded wives, and worshiped pagan gods, but we found them kind, generous, and without guile. They treated us like family, and, unlike the untrustworthy chicleros, the Lacandon never stole.

One day Carl told me a story that was so bizarre it was hard to believe. It happened sometime in the early '40s when the dictator Jorge Ubico, popularly known as "Tata" (Spanish for daddy), ruled Guatemala. Soldiers from Guatemala crossed the border into Mexico and captured two Lacandon

Ko

Carmita (NaBor)

Indians, manacled them, and took them back to the zoo in Guatemala City and locked them in a cage. When Mexican government officials learned that two Lacandon Indians were on exhibit at the zoo they were furious and immediately contacted their embassy in Guatemala and swiftly obtained the Indians' release.

We gave ChanBor the Victrola and showed him how he could sharpen dull phonograph needles using a stone. His favorite records were the operas, which he played over and over. He especially liked Caruso arias; however, the jazz and ranchero music didn't seem to interest him at all.

He was so pleased with his new toy he agreed to take us to a very special ruin the Lacandon kept secret. This place, only three hours away by foot, turned out to be the now famous ruins known to the world as Bonampak, or Painted Walls, a name given to the site by the famous Maya archaeologist Sylvanus Griswold Morley. Actually, Bonampak is literally translated as "vat-dyed" or "tanned," as in fabric or leather.

One chiclero, Acasio Chan, was already at the caribal, but we needed one more helper, so we sent word to El Cedro for another chiclero to accompany us. The young man they sent, Luís Huchin, was a half-witted Yucatec Maya from Vallodolid, Yucatán. He was clumsy with our gear but was able to follow simple directions. Once he arrived, the four of us started our trek to the ruins. ChanBor led the way, and the chicleros carried our supplies.

After an hour we came to a wide river and crossed the surging rapids astride a slippery, moss-covered log. ChanBor was the only one agile enough to walk it like a professional tightrope artist.

Later that morning, we crossed the same river again, this time following a four-inch-wide ledge on the lip of a twenty-foot high waterfall. I stared straight ahead, afraid if I looked down I would lose my balance and plummet over the falls. Fortunately, despite the precarious location, the water was less than an inch deep, so there was little chance of being pushed over the rim by the current.

ChanKin posing with two chicleros

About ten minutes from the ruins, close to a small encampment of chicle gatherers, Acasio found an abandoned hut and we unloaded our gear. Carl said the chicleros looked like a bunch of escaped convicts. The meanest one must have been in a machete fight at one time because he had a nasty scar starting where an ear should have been and ending at his collar bone. We both wondered if they were the same escaped convicts we had heard about who were hiding from the Mexican authorities.

On February 6 we headed west across a shallow stream and got our first glimpse of the ruins. The first building we saw was a large, well-preserved temple on the top of an overgrown platform. We named this Structure 1. The building had three doorways that led to a small, empty room with a plaster floor covered in a thick layer of bat guano. On a steep terraced hillside behind Structure 1 there were six smaller buildings that we numbered 2 through 7.

Four of these temples contained columnar stone altars set in the plastered floor. Structure 4 had a beautifully carved stone lintel depicting the bust of a dignitary holding a ceremonial bar and wearing an elaborate headdress of quetzal plumes. Hieroglyphic panels decorated both sides and there were four more glyphs next to the profile. On one of the side exterior walls, just below the coping, were two wide bands

Structure 1 at Bonampak

Plan, by John Bourne, of temples at Bonampak

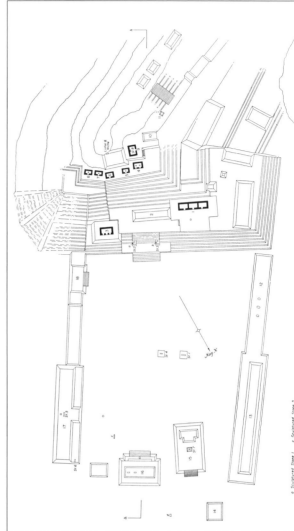

Plan of Bonampak taken from Carnegie Institution Publication 602

Buildings on level 2

Niche in a hill behind Structure 4

painted blood red. On the lower part of the right door jamb of Structure 4, Carl and I scratched our names in small letters on the plastered wall. In a cliff behind Structure 4, a rubble-filled niche looked like it might be an opening to a shallow cave.

Structure 6 had a high roof comb that had once been decorated with stucco reliefs. The two doorways of this building framed interior columnar stone altars. Just around the corner from this temple was a large building, Structure 7, with a corbeled roof and a large, half-fallen, stone lintel.

I had brought along a Brunton compass and a fifty-foot tape measure, and Huchin helped me measure Structure 1 on the lower level, and the six temples on the terraced platform behind it, which I sketched in my notebook. All the dimensions were correctly recorded, but because I was so weak from the onset of malarial fever at the time, I was barely able to scrawl an outline of each building. To further document the site I had the two chicleros clear brush from around the temples, and then I loaded my camera with film and snapped different views of each building.

As I was busy mapping the site, Carl and Acasio were hacking down jungle growth just west of Structure 1. This was in the same area where four months later Healey found the temple with the fabulous murals. Both Carl and Acasio were working in that same location for hours, and to this day I don't see how they could have missed it. The temple with the murals turned out to be only 115 feet west of Structure 1.

We had been working at the ruin for two days when Chan-Bor came to warn us that chicleros at a nearby camp planned to kill us while we were asleep. They wanted our money, our watches, and my camera. Heeding their warning we quickly packed our things and quietly slipped away, following the same trail back to the Lacandon caribal. In the middle of the sunlit path, a fer-de-lance was coiled and ready to strike. This large and venomous pit viper is common to the American tropics, and I was about to step on it. I was so startled I let out a yell and jumped high into the air, scaring it—and everyone else—deep into the forest shadows.

That night Carl and I sat around a campfire. After removing our boots and socks we discovered our feet were covered

View of roof comb on Structure 6

with nigua bites. The tiny insects had burrowed deep into our callused feet and laid their eggs. Our toes and heels were infested with egg sacks, and to extract them we had to use the tip of a knife to cut out the sacks and then pour tincture of Merthiolate into the raw, sore openings to prevent infection. We returned to El Cedro the next day and started unpacking the recording equipment. After running a test, we found the generator made a racket and the microphone was picking it up; so before we started recording, we placed the generator 200 feet away from the SoundScriber. When we checked it again and found that the microphone was still picking up sound from the generator, we placed the generator in a hole dug behind office headquarters and covered the opening with palm leaves to muffle the noise.

The Lacandon watched, spellbound, as we tested the equipment. Once everything was in working order, we started recording their chants and flute music. When we played the recordings back to them, their faces lit up. They recognized their voices and suddenly broke into embarrassed laughter.

By this time I had such a severe case of malaria and amoebic dysentery that I could barely keep anything down. Yet for some reason I had an insatiable craving for Nestlé's condensed milk and consumed more than eight cans of it a day. In a short time I used up the chicle camp's supply and asked the jefe to have the plane fly in another case of Nestlé's.

Watercolor illustration of Bonampak, Structure 1, Room 2, South Wall, by Heather Hurst and Leonard Ashby, Bonampak Documentation Project

The thick liquid helped to coat my stomach but the cramps became unbearable, and the camp mule doctor had to give me an injection of Metina for the dysentery. The medicine is supposed to be injected intramuscularly, but ignoring directions, the "doctor" made several jabs into my arm with a dull needle, working it back and forth under the skin until he finally hit a vein and injected the medicine directly into it.

Being young—and fortunate—I survived both the illness and the cure.

One day, a replacement chiclero arrived in camp. He was only a teenager and was making his first trip into the jungle to tap chicle trees. He made the tragic mistake of confusing a sapling chechem tree for a chicle tree. With the first slash of his machete a white fluid squirted onto his face and into his

Rear view of headquarters at El Cedro

Kayom with his flute

Recording Kayom playing his flute

eyes. The fluid was so corrosive that it immediately started to burn his skin and eyes. We knew that overnight the sap would eat into his eyes and face and slowly blind him. A Lacandon man who was visiting the camp said it would help to flush his eyes with human urine, but this did nothing. Then one of the chicleros took a pinch of chili powder and sprinkled it into the teenager's bloodshot eyes. The boy screamed and writhed in pain, and to keep him from falling on the floor the mule doctor had him tied to the bedposts. As sick as I felt, I couldn't bear to listen to his screams any longer and grabbed my hammock and went to the hut by the airstrip. The next morning the jefe told us that the boy was completely blind.

We heard that Healey had found out that Carl and I were back at El Cedro looking for ruins. He had notified the authorities in Merida that we were digging in the temples and were removing Maya antiquities. Of course the charges were false. In fact at one ruin we had gathered together the parts of a stucco figure and chunks of stucco carvings that had fallen from a façade and placed them inside the temple to protect them from the elements. As for stealing objects from the temples, there was some speculation that Healey may have been referring to Lacandon "god" pots, although I didn't believe the pots were what he meant. These pots are almost the only removable items we found at the ruins. While they may have been around fifty to a hundred years old, they definitely were not Maya antiquities.

On Tuesday, February 12, Carl and I, following the reports of local chicleros, discovered another important ruin which

The jefe of the chicle camp (left) and John Bourne standing beside the Cedro River

Stucco fragments

Fragments of a stucco arm

we measured and photographed. The Carnegie Institution later named the site Lacanhá. It was located just below the confluence of the Cedro and Lacanhá Rivers. I won't go into detail except to say that it was extremely unusual to find a building in this region with two round columns dividing the entrance. We named the site "Round Column." Not far from this building we also found and photographed a circular altar with carved glyphs. When we inspected the interior wall of the one standing temple we noticed that while most of the plaster had fallen to the floor and crumbled, there were a few places where colored wall paintings still clung to the stone surface.

On this last trip I became so weak from malaria and dysentery that I kept falling off my mule. Carl finally had to rope me to the animal until we got back to the chicle camp. Once there we began packing our things, as a plane was due to arrive early the next morning. The jefe handed us a bill which included the cost of food, mules, and hired hands. For the thirty-six days that we had been in camp "and on the road," the total bill came to $34.77 U.S., that's a daily cost of only 49 cents per person.

ChanKin and a few other Lacandon had gathered inside the small hut next to the airstrip to see us off. Two small

children squatted by a fire, puffing on large cigars made of native tobacco. We still had a few trinkets left and bargained with the men for bows, arrows and a colton, belonging to ChanKin.

On our return to Mexico City Carl and I wasted no time taking our film to be developed. We had the camera shop, Photo Gante, make two copies of every shot. On March 14, 1946, Carl reported the ruins to Sr. Juan Palacios of the Instituto Nacional de Antropologia e História, and I left for the United States.

On May 24 I wrote Dr. Alfred Kidder at the Carnegie Institution of Washington. It was my first letter to him, and it stated that Carl and I had found several important ruins in Chiapas in February 1946. At the time, Dr. Kidder was in Guatemala, and his secretary, Eleanor Ritchie, wrote back saying he wouldn't return until July.

When Healey went back to El Cedro in May 1946, he heard about our discoveries and was taken to the first ruin Carl and I had seen on February 6, 1946. It was then he was shown the building with the paintings. A few months later I received a letter from Carl, saying he had gone back to El Cedro when Healey was there, and that was the first time he had seen the murals.

Temple with round columns at the site of Lacanhá

In July 1946, I sent Dr. Kidder my map of Bonampak, drawn to scale, and included Photostats of all seven structures. He answered on October 9, 1946, and said he had received the Photostats on July 30 and was looking forward to seeing my photographs and drawings of the buildings.

Meanwhile Healey had written Kidder of his find. At the time, Dr. Kidder didn't realize that Healey's discoveries were of the same ruins that I had already reported to him. It wasn't until June 1947 that Dr. Kidder first recognized that the site Carl and I had discovered and the ruins in which Healey had found the murals were one and the same. In late June 1947, just after Dr. Kidder and Dr. Karl Ruppert of the Carnegie Institution realized that Carl and I were the first explorers to visit the site, Healey's discovery of the murals made headlines in *Life* and *Time* magazines. The murals had received so much publicity, not only because they were remarkable examples of Maya art, but because they also disproved previous contentions that the Maya were an entirely peaceful civilization.

Carl and I finally did get recognition for all the ruins we had discovered but not until 1955, when an account entitled "Bonampak, Chiapas, Mexico" was published in the Carnegie Institution of Washington Publication 602.

I received a letter from Carl, dated June 7, 1947, informing me that our names were still up when he returned to Bonampak in October 1946; however, later that year a Mexican painter told Carl only Healey's name was there. In his letter Carl said he thought Healey was behaving childishly by erasing our names from the stuccoed door jamb.

A letter came from Dr. Karl Ruppert, dated June 20, 1947, in which he states: "When I was in Bonampak this last season we made a surveyed map of the site using a transit. Your plan so closely coincides with ours I wonder if you had a transit." In my reply to him I wrote that I didn't have a transit and had taken all the measurements and bearings using only a tape measure and a compass.

A thirteen-member expedition, led by Carl Frey, organized by the Instituto Nacional de Bellas Artes, and including artist Franco Gomez, arrived at Bonampak in April 1949. On May 3, the canoe carrying Franco Gomez overturned in the Lacanhá River, and Carl jumped in and attempted to save him. Both were killed in the rapids.

I heard that Carl was buried in the jungle, near the scene of the accident. This account is dedicated to his memory.

Carl Frey

ADDENDUM

Maya dates given in the Carnegie Institution of Washington Publication 602 follow:

At OXLAHUNTUN: Modeled in stucco on a masonry pier to the right of the central doorway of one of the temples is the recorded Initial Series date 9.13.0.0.0 8 Ahau 8 Uo. In the Gregorian Calendar the date corresponds to March 16, 692 AD.

At MIGUEL ANGEL FERNANDEZ: No calendric data is given for this site in Publication 602.

At BONAMPAK: Lintel of Structure 6 (4 in our numbering) records the Calendar Round Date 9.8.9.15.11 7 Chuen 4 Zotz', the same as May 13, 603 AD. It is possible, however, that the position falls one Maya Calendar Round (fifty-two years) later, or 9.11.2.10.11 7 Chuen 4 Zotz', the equivalent of April 30, 655 AD.

At LACANHÁ: Stela 7 records three dates:
9.8.0.0.0 5 Ahau 3 Che'n, or August 22, 593 AD
9.6.0.11.0 8 Ahau 18 Zac, or October 26, 554 AD
9.9.0.11.0 2 Ahau 3 Muan, or December 15, 613 AD

Photographs, negatives, and drawings of the ruins, and pictures of the Lacandon, as well as letters from Carl Frey, Dr. Kidder, and Dr. Ruppert, are in the archives of the Walters Art Museum, Baltimore.

Recordings of the Lacandon chants and flute music were remastered and recorded on tape and then transferred to compact disc in 1999. These are also in the archives of the Walters Art Museum.

COPY OF ORIGINAL EL CEDRO BILL

RELACION DEL GASTOS PAGADOS EN ESTE CENTRAL CEDRO. CHIS NEGOCIACION DEL SR. FELIPE RIANCHO POR EL SR. JOHN BOURNE DURANTE SU ESTANCIA

Por alimentacion de John Bourne y Carlos Frey D/31 Enero/4 Feb a - $3.00 Diarios c/u[1] .... $ 30.00

Por jornales de Luis Huchin D/4/12 Feb a $3.00 Drs 27.00

Por alimentacion de John Bourne y Carlos Frey D/12/19 Feb. a $3.00 Diarios c/u 48.00

Por jornales de Enrique Frey[2] D-19/22 Feb. a $4.00 Dris 16.00

Por alimentacion de John Bourne y Carlos Frey D 22/2 de marzo, a $3.00 diarios c/u 54.00

Por alquiler 3 bestias D-19/22 Feb. a $3.00 c/u 36.00

Por alimentacion de John Bourne y Carlos Frey D/4/7 marzo a $3.00 diarios c/u 24.00

Por jornales de Victor Rivero D/2/4 de marzo a $3.00 Drs. 9.00

Valor mercancias tomo tienda Cedro. S/g.[3] Diarios 190.64

Suma Total .... $ 434.64

[signature]

Marzo 7 de 1946   C. Cedro Chis.
                    Pedro Aldecon F.

ENGLISH TRANSLATION OF THE EL CEDRO BILL

ACCOUNT OF EXPENDITURES PAID IN THIS CEDRO OFFICE. CHIS. NEGOTIATED BY SR. FELIPE RIANCHO FOR MR. JOHN BOURNE DURING HIS STAY

For meals for John Bourne and Carl Frey D/31 January/4 Feb. at $3.00 a day each .... $ 30.00

For wages of Luis Huchin D/4/12 Feb. at $3.00 daily 27.00

For meals for John Bourne and Carl Frey D/12/19 Feb. at $3.00 a day each 48.00

For wages of Enrique Frey D-19/22 Feb. at $4.00 a day 16.00

For meals for John Bourne and Carl Frey D 22/2 of March, at $3.00 a day each 54.00

For hire of 3 mules D-19/22 Feb. at $3.00 each 36.00

For meals for John Bourne and Carl Frey D/4/7 March at $3.00 a day each 24.00

For wages of Victor Rivero D/2/4 for March at $3.00 a day 9.00

Price of merchandise from Cedro stock room daily draft 190.64

Sum total .... $ 434.64

[signature]

March 7, 1946   C. Cedro Chis.
                    Pedro Aldecon F.

COMMENTS

Carl and I spent thirty-six days in Lacanhá, from January 31, 1946 to March 7, 1946. The rate of exchange was then 12.5 pesos to the dollar, which comes to $34.74 total. Our daily cost was 97 cents, or 49 cents a day per person.

NOTES

1. The abbreviation c/u, "cada uno," translates as "each."

2. Enrique Frey was not related to Carl Frey.

3. The abbreviation S/g, "Su giro," means "your draft" or "your bill of exchange."

1946 COUNT OF LACANDON FAMILIES
LIVING IN THE LACANHÁ AREA

In the Lacanhá area the number of Lacandon in the five caribals consisted of seven males and eighteen females, or a total of twenty-five individuals. Chicleros from the El Cedro camp gave Spanish names to a number of Lacandon with whom they had the most contact.

• denotes Lacandon who were photographed

¤ denotes Lacandon who made recordings

Caribal 1

M•¤	ChanKin (Obregón), patriarch
F •	NahaKin 1, mother of ChanKin (Obregón)
F	NahaKin 2, wife of ChanKin (Obregón)
F •¤	NaBor 1, wife of ChanKin (Obregón) and sister of ChanBor (José Pépe)
F •	Carmita 1, age 14, sister of ChanKin (Obregón)
F	Margarita, sister of ChanKin (Obregón)
F •	Ko, age 8
M	Kayom 1, child
F	NahaKin 3, child

9 Lacandon in Caribal 1

Caribal 2

M•	ChanBor (José Pépe), patriarch
F •	NahaKin 4 (Carmita), wife of ChanBor (José Pépe)
F •	NaBor 2 (Rosita 1) wife of ChanBor (José Pépe)

3 Lacandon in Caribal 2

Caribal 3

M•¤	Kayom 2, patriarch
F •	NaBor 3, wife of Kayom 2 and sister of ChanBor (José Pépe)
F	NahaKin 5, wife of Kayom 2 and sister of ChanBor (José Pépe)

3 Lacandon in Caribal 3

Caribal 4

M•	Bor, patriarch
F	Rosita 2, wife of Bor
F	Nunc, child of Rosita 2
M	Kin, child of Rosita 2

4 Lacandon in Caribal 4

Caribal 5

M•	Kayom 3 (Carranza), patriarch
F	Maria, mother of Kayom 3
F	Name not recorded, wife of Kayom 3
F	Name not recorded, wife of Kayom 3
F	Name not recorded, wife of Kayom 3
F	Baby, name not recorded, child of Kayom 3

6 Lacandon in Caribal 5

NOTE TO THE READER

The catalogue that follows describes works from the collection of John Bourne given or promised to the Walters Art Museum and exhibited at the museum from February 12, 2012 through May 20, 2012. It also includes loans to the Walters by the Los Angeles County Museum of Art and the New Mexico History Museum of objects given to these institutions by Mr. Bourne. The balance of the collection gift is documented in the checklist (pp. 204–45).

The dates given in the following entries begin with the name of the culture period followed by the period's entire date-spread. In some instances, it is possible to narrow the date-spread on the basis of stylistic, archaeological, or hieroglyphic data. Thus, for example, an artwork made during the Middle Formative Period, which spans the centuries 900–300 BCE, may be noted as dating from 900–600 BCE based on specific historical data or the piece's artistic style.

The attribution of works in the John Bourne Collection is based on an ongoing study of their style, iconography, manufacture, and materials. Objects that cannot be confidently authenticated as of ancient American manufacture, or that are so heavily restored that their authenticity is moot, are signaled by the absence of a date range. Those objects that the book's authors believe to be not authentic are also indicated by the addition of the word "style" after that of the culture (e.g., Olmec Style).

The Walters Art Museum's acquisitions and accessions are informed by the museum's commitment to:

DUE DILIGENCE: The acquisition of a work of art will be conducted with consideration of full and rigorous investigation and documentation of the work's provenance and authenticity. Research is ongoing, and if new evidence emerges on the provenance of any work, it will be presented on our website.

TRANSPARENCY: The work, whether gifted, purchased or received as a long-term loan and/or planned gift, will be promptly published in full on the Walters' website and on the Object Registry of the Association of Art Museum Directors (aamdobjectregistry.org).

GOOD-FAITH ENGAGEMENT: The museum will promptly and openly respond to any claims for repatriation of the work from possible source countries.

Gary Vikan
Director, The Walters Art Museum

Texas

MEXICO

Gulf of Mexico

HUASTEC

NAYARIT

• Ixtlán
del Río

R. Lerma

• El Tajín

CHUPÍCUARO

TEOTIHUACAN

Chupícuaro •

JALISCO

Teotihuacan •

MEXICA
(AZTEC)

Tlatilco •

COLIMA

Tenochtitlan

• • Tlapacoya

• Remojades

• El Zapotal

• Cholula

REMOJADES

R. Balsas

MEZCALA

Xochipala • • Teopantecuanitlán

OLMEC

MIXTECA

• Monte Albán

ZAPOTEC

PACIFIC OCEAN

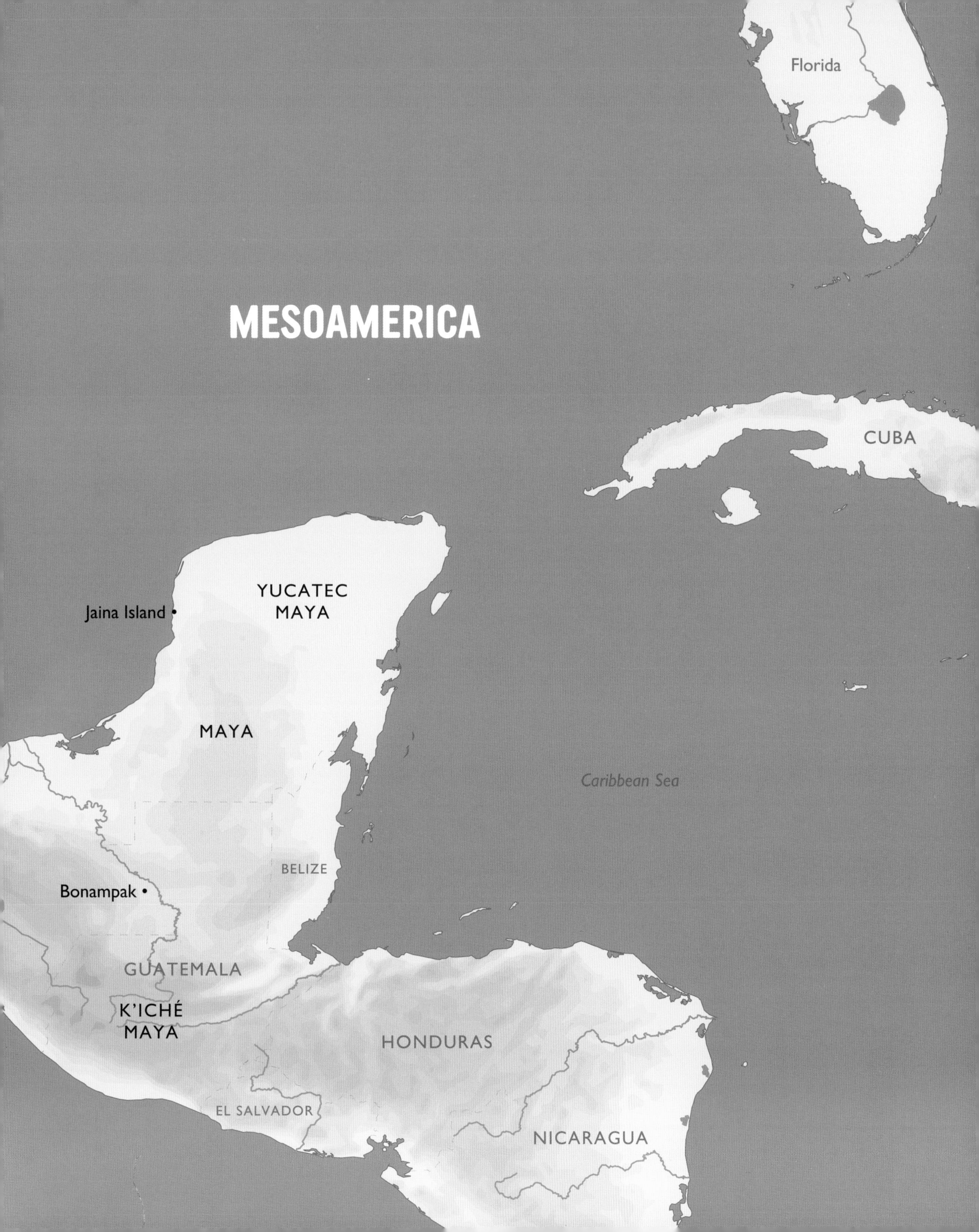

MESOAMERICA

Florida

CUBA

Caribbean Sea

YUCATEC
MAYA

Jaina Island •

MAYA

BELIZE

Bonampak •

GUATEMALA

K'ICHÉ
MAYA

HONDURAS

EL SALVADOR

NICARAGUA

MESOAMERICA

Ancient Mesoamerica's agricultural revolution commenced before 5000 BCE, when the region's farmers began producing the nutritious powerhouse of maize (corn), beans, and squash. These wonderful foods provided the carbohydrates and proteins that fueled the rapid development of one of the world's great civilizations. Mesoamerica's many other foods, including chocolate, vanilla, tomatoes, avocados, and chiles, transformed the world's gastronomy, from Szechuan and Italian cuisines to the famous chocolates of Belgium. Occupying the present-day nations of Mexico, Belize, Guatemala, and the northern portions of Honduras and El Salvador, ancient Mesoamerica embodied a unique social, political, intellectual, and ideological manifestation of human culture. Its many peoples, speaking myriad languages, devised marvels of engineering, mathematics, writing, and the arts. They probed the many dimensions of human spirituality, exploring the common realm of the unknowable shared by all peoples.

Modern historians divide ancient Mesoamerican history into three main periods. The Formative or Preclassic Period (1200 BCE–100 CE) witnessed the rise of Mesoamerica's first principal culture, known as the Olmecs. They are credited with initiating many of the political, economic, social, and intellectual advances that define Mesoamerican civilization. The Olmecs developed a religion that embraced the ancient ideology of shamanism—the belief in spirit companion forms into which the specially empowered practitioner can transform him/her self. In this spirit form, often represented in Mesoamerican art as the combination of human and animal features, the shaman may harness supernatural powers to wield on earth—to heal the sick, ensure the earth's fertility, and even vanquish political enemies. Olmec rulers often are portrayed adorned with motifs that indicate their shamanic powers as well as the gods' benediction of their right to rule. From this time onward, divine kingship was the foundation of political power throughout Mesoamerica.

The subsequent Classic Period (100–900 CE) witnessed a cultural efflorescence throughout Mesoamerica, with distinctive societies taking control of particular regions while interacting with neighboring ones. International connections, focused primarily on trade and economic expansion, developed with cultures near and far—from northern Mexico and the southwestern United States, to Central America, and even as far south as Ecuador. The preeminent Classic Period society was Teotihuacan, located in the central highlands northeast of present-day Mexico City. The Teotihuacan metropolis was one of the world's largest urban zones in the fifth century, surpassed only by Beijing. More than 120,000 people lived in the city, which was laid out on a precise grid pattern; even the valley's river was rechanneled to conform to this grid. The main thoroughfare, the so-called Avenue of the Dead, was punctuated by massive, highly decorated buildings, whose size and colorful ornamentation must have awed and even overwhelmed those who saw the city at its zenith. Until the completion of New York City's Empire State Building in 1931, Teotihuacan's Pyramid of the Sun was the tallest structure in the Americas. Although the city was destroyed in the seventh century, by a combination of internal conflict and outside opportunism, memory of Teotihuacan's grandeur survived in the mythology of the Aztecs more than nine hundred years later. They were so impressed by the ruined city's enormous scale that they believed it was here the gods created the present fifth age of the world. They christened it

"Teotihuacan," which in Nahuatl, the language of the Aztecs, means "City of the Gods."

Other dynamic Classic Period cultures include the Zapotecs of southern Mexico and those of the Gulf Coast. Each developed unique artistic and architectural styles and novel interpretations of pan-Mesoamerican cultural traditions. In Veracruz and northern Tabasco, the art of the Gulf Coast cultures is distinguished by large, hollow figural sculptures in ceramic, some of which were buried in narrative groups, that depict rituals or express religious beliefs. Others portray religious practitioners in ecstatic trances. Zapotec architecture is expansive in form, imitating the wide, mountainous vistas surrounding its urban centers in the modern Mexican state of Oaxaca. Elaborate tombs of the aristocracy were filled with figural sculptures, finely crafted pottery, jadeite body adornments, and many items made of perishable materials that have not survived. Carved stone monuments include pictorial and hieroglyphic records of the deeds of Zapotec rulers and their connections to the divine.

West Mexico, as an ancient cultural region, was home to relatively independent societies during the Early Classic Period, far removed from the heart of Mesoamerica yet sharing many cultural features with their distant cultural cousins. The region is renowned for lively and distinctive ceramic sculptures, unequaled in their imaginative variety of renderings of the human figure. The peoples' ancient appellations have not survived, prompting modern scholars to name the various art styles after the modern Mexican states where the artworks have been found. It is likely that at least some of these Classic Period societies were the ancestors of the Tarascans, the region's dominant culture after 1000 CE. Jalisco,

Nayarit, and Colima pottery styles, created a thousand years earlier, feature diverse figural sculptures and food-service vessels modeled in naturalistic forms; they typically are found in deep shaft tombs having multiple burial chambers filled with funerary offerings. Archaeological evidence suggests that each tomb belonged to a family of high status, and only the top-ranked members of the lineage would have been honored with burial in the lineage tomb. The unique shaft-tomb form, the appearance of metallurgy as a fully developed technology sometime before 700 CE, and the unusual stirrup-spout vessel form constitute some of the evidence implying seafaring contacts between West Mexico and peoples of Colombia and coastal Ecuador, where similar burial modes, pottery forms, and materials technologies were first developed.

The Classic Period Maya of southern Mesoamerica built a vigorous culture, sharing many of the key features of Mesoamerican civilization. Yet they are set apart by unique art and architecture. The Classic Maya are especially renowned for their hieroglyphic writing system with which they recorded human history, astronomy and astrology, mythology, and religious ideals. Tragically, none of the Classic Period books (called "codices") have survived, and the invading Spanish burned hundreds of Postclassic books that contained the historical, intellectual, and spiritual knowledge of thousands of years of human development in Mesoamerica. Hieroglyphic texts nonetheless survive from the Classic Period, carved on stone monuments and painted on the fantastic pictorial pottery. In their technical skill, narrative content, and aesthetics, Classic Maya painted ceramics rival the world's finest low-fired, painted pottery traditions, including that of ancient Greece. They also are a principal source of data concerning innumerable facets of Maya cultural history, recounting in text and image religious precepts, mythology, and political history that survives nowhere else.

The Postclassic Period (900–1521 CE) heralded dramatic changes throughout Mesoamerica. Many of the Classic Period powers diminished, and their cities, such as Teotihuacan, fell into ruin; new players ascended to the now-vacant sociopolitical stage. Changes in the ideology of kingship were central to the era's shift of power, including the demise of sacred kings among the Classic Period Maya. Their magnificent cities in the southern lowlands were reclaimed by the jungle, and Maya civilization shifted to Mexico's Yucatan Peninsula with its impressive metropolises at Chichén Itzá and Mayapán. At the time of Spanish contact in the sixteenth century, the cities of Yucatan were major centers of trade and commerce, politics, and learning.

The Aztecs, who called themselves the Mexica, were the final dominant culture in central Mexico when the Spanish arrived on the Gulf Coast in 1519 CE. The Aztecs emerged from their northern desert homeland and settled in the populous Valley of Mexico in 1325 CE. They embarked on an extraordinary path to control the valley by 1428 CE and, during the ensuing decades, extended their politico-economic control east, south, and west. Conquering its neighbors by warfare, coercion, and persuasion, the Mexica Empire was Mesoamerica's largest and richest. Animosity toward the Aztecs' heavy tax burdens and occasional strong-arm politics prompted various peoples to assist the invading Spanish. Little did they know that these newcomers sought not only to overthrow the Aztecs but also to take control of the social, economic, and spiritual lives of all Mesoamerican peoples. Yet in spite of the Spanish eradication of the native societies, the strength of this great civilization is reflected in its survivals in matters of daily routines, foods and cuisines, politics, religion, and modern national identities of the five nations that constitute today's Mesoamerica.

Note

1. Kelly 1974. See also von Winning 1974, 18–19; Anawalt 1998.

I. FEMALE FIGURE

Morelos or Puebla, Mexico
Early Formative Period, 1200–900 BCE
Earthenware, burnished slip paint
39.9 × 17.8 × 7.1 cm
2009.20.50

2. FEMALE FIGURE

Morelos or Puebla, Mexico
Early Formative Period, 1200–900 BCE
Earthenware, burnished slip paint
50.7 × 18.9 × 8.2 cm
2009.20.52

Large, hollow figures epitomize the sculptural expertise of the earliest pottery artists in the central Mexican highlands. Found in burials at sites in the Valley of Mexico, such as Tlatilco and Tlapacoya, and many others in the adjacent states of Morelos and Puebla, these figures typically portray nude women. Artists accentuate the hips and firm breasts while reducing the arms and feet to small, simplified forms. This corporeal focus has prompted some scholars to interpret them as fertility objects pertaining to female rites of passage or fecundity.

An alternative view sees the figures as representations of religious practitioners in the throes of shamanic trance. This interpretation calls attention to the artistic accentuation of the head and the careful rendering of elaborate head wraps or coiffures. Frequently, too, these figures' mouths are rendered slightly open and their eyes stare blankly into space. These features recall renderings of shamanic trance throughout the Americas. Both figures have scored ears, which the Spanish observed among many Native priests in highland Mexico and Yucatan, cut during blood-offering rituals that served both religious ideology and the achievement of a spiritual trance state.

3

3. STANDING FEMALE FIGURE

Teopantecuanitlán area, Guerrero, Mexico

Middle Formative Period, 900–600 BCE

Earthenware, post-fire paint/pigment (red, white, and black), incising

13.1 × 4.3 × 2.6 cm

TL.2009.20.253

4. SEATED MALE FIGURE

Teopantecuanitlán area, Guerrero, Mexico

Early Formative Period, 1200–900 BCE

Earthenware, post-fire paint/pigment (red, white, and black), incising

8 × 5.9 × 6.8 cm

TL.2009.20.254

Solid, hand-modeled figurines of diminutive size yet remarkable detail and expressiveness represent the Xochipala style, a distinctive artistic tradition found in the highlands of Guerrero in western Mexico. The standing female figure dates to the middle centuries of the Middle Formative Period, when artists adorned the figurines with much more personal regalia than is found in earlier works.

The seated figure's lack of adornment and the marked figural naturalism are characteristic of early works from this period.

The standing female seems to depict an adolescent girl wearing the style's typical pubic wrap with front and rear tufts. A long braid falls down her back, which is decorated with incised motifs (fig. 1). Her wide eyes and slightly opened mouth imply an ecstatic state.

The seated male figure holds a long bar, perhaps a scepter denoting political status. Large tufts adorn the tops of his feet, and his loins are wrapped in a red-painted cloth, the only surviving vestige of the region's textile arts. Both figures sport large ear flares, and their hair is indicated by sharply incised lines. Slashes on their shoulders likely represent body paint, tattoos, or intentional scarring, a type of body adornment seen on many later ceramic figural sculptures from western Mexico.

Technical Commentary

The hair, ear spools, clothing, and hand-held accouterments of these hand-modeled figures were added to the main form in separate applications of clay, as were the lips, eyelids, and noses. A pointed tool was used to create hollows of the pupils and navel. The detailed incision work of both figures was done while the clay was still wet.

The clay of both figures is notable for its large and numerous quartz inclusions. The resulting rough texture is partially covered by post-fire paint. Mercury, detected using x-ray fluorescence, was identified in the red pigment used to paint portions of both figures and is likely a natural form of cinnabar. The use of cinnabar and other post-fire paints, including white and black, found on these figures has been observed on other excavated examples.[1] Analyses of white paint on the standing figure indicate a calcium-based pigment; the absence of coloring agents such as iron or manganese in the black pigment may indicate the use of a carbon-based black. Traces of arsenic on both figures cannot be directly linked to a pigment color; it seems to be in highest concentration in white-painted areas (JL).[2]

Fig. 1. Incision work on back of no. 3

4

Notes

1. Reference to the use of "cinnabar" red and white and black and yellow "ochre" paints on other Xochipala figurines can be found in Griffin 1972, 306.

2. Elevated levels of calcium and arsenic were detected in areas painted white using nondestructive XRF.

5. FEMALE FIGURINE

Chupícuaro, Guanajuato, Mexico
Late Formative Period, 300–100 BCE
Earthenware, post-fire paint (red)
8.9 × 4.8 × 2.5 cm
TL.2009.20.226

6. SEATED MALE FIGURE

Chupícuaro, Guanajuato, Mexico
Late Formative Period, 300–100 BCE
Earthenware, post-fire paint
5.7 × 3.8 × 1.9 cm
TL.2009.20.234

Famous for their diminutive size and fine details, Chupícuaro figurines emphasize rounded body contours and triangular faces accented by elongated, slanted eyes. Often the artists contrast the smoothness of skin with striations indicating hair, garnishing the coiffures with red pigment. Many figurines sport elaborate necklaces and ear ornaments; woven bands or hats sometimes adorn their heads. The seated figure may represent a player of the Mesoamerican ballgame, suggested by the wide band protecting his right forearm and the rounded-top hat.

Chupícuaro figurines' functions are not well understood. They typically are found in burials, common domestic contexts, and non-architectural settings such as agricultural fields. A theme of fertility is implied by the majority depicting women, often with realistically rendered genitalia and generously rounded abdomens. Regardless of their ancient function, the figurines constitute a detailed source of information concerning Chupícuaro body adornment and hairstyles, and their expressive delicacy implies an appreciation of fine craftsmanship.

7. RITUAL CELT

Olmec, Mexico

Early to Middle Formative Periods, 1200–600 BCE

Jadeite (?)

38.2 × 9.5 × 6.8 cm

TL.2009.20.288

Carved in the form of the primary field-clearing tool, the chopping celt, this enlarged version made from precious green stone connotes the power of the ruler who wielded it. Its functional reference and its green color imply the ruler's shamanic ability and responsibility to ensure agricultural success. The celt form as a ritual object also alludes to decapitation sacrifices for the gods who controlled nature and the growth of crops.[1]

Celts are occasionally found in burials, but most come from ritual deposits placed in pyramids, plazas, and sacred springs. The caches often contain a large number of celts arranged in rows or geometric patterns, and sometimes laid within specially colored clay or sand.[2] Most celts are plain, as is this example, but others are incised with images of Olmec deities such as the maize god.[3] The celt's seedlike shape, green color, and its "planting" in the ground indicate an agricultural ceremonial meaning for these special deposits. The multiple references to fertility, regeneration, and maintenance of the balance of nature would have had powerful connotations for the person wielding the ceremonial celt as an implement of political office.

Notes

1. Washington 1996, 264, nos. 112–13 (E. Benson).

2. Stirling and Stirling 1942. See also San Francisco 2010, 132–39, pls. 33–48 (M. del Carmen Rodríguez and P. Ortíz Ceballos).

3. Fields 1989.

8. MASKETTE PENDANT

Olmec style, Gulf Coast, Mexico

Jadeite[1]

2.2 × 2 × 0.5 cm

TL.2009.20.231

9. SKULL EFFIGY PENDANT

Maya, Pacific Slopes, Guatemala

Late Preclassic Period, 300 BCE–100 CE

Burnished earthenware

6.5 × 3.7 × 1.9 cm

TL.2009.20.221

The Olmecs were among the world's finest carvers of jadeite, a very hard stone that they worked without the advantage of metal tools. The remarkable thinness of this tiny mask (no. 8) emphasizes the stunning translucency of the blue-green mineral. Worn as body adornment, the pendant renders the typical Olmec-style face with wide, flat nose and down-turned mouth recalling a jaguar's snarl. This combination of human and animal features is an Olmec artistic convention for depicting supernatural beings. As the portrayal of a spirit being or god, the pendant would imply the wearer's connection to the supernatural. The high quality of the jadeite and its exceptionally fine carving indicate the wearer's high status.

The equally small skull effigy pendant (no. 9) was made nearly 600 years later by the Maya of the Pacific Slopes of Guatemala. Similar in size, artistic quality, imagery, and function to the earlier Olmec pendant, this

expressive ornament demonstrates the continuity among later Mesoamerican peoples of body adornments functioning as symbols of identity, status, and power. This remarkably delicate pendant connotes the Mesoamerican ideology of death and rebirth as a central principle of the universe's natural cycle. It may also pertain to the shamanic journey between worlds, the shaman's passage to the supernatural realm being likened to death and rebirth.[2]

Notes

1. Nondestructive Raman analysis was used to identify the stone. The analysis was carried out by Catherine Matsen, conservation scientist at the Scientific Research and Analysis Laboratory of the Winterthur Museum and Country Estate, Wilmington, Delaware.

2. Stone-Miller 2002b, xviii–xx.

8

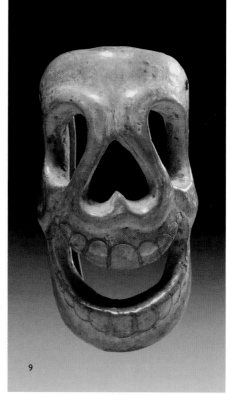

9

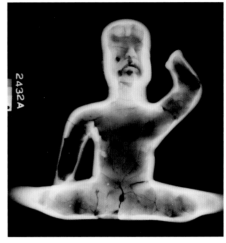

Fig. 1. X-ray, showing original adjoining fragments

10. INFANTILE FIGURE

Olmec, Central Highlands, Mexico
Early Formative Period, 1200–900 BCE
Earthenware, burnished slip, post-fire paint (red)
31.1 × 33.3 × 16 cm
2009.20.64

Hollow figures portraying a seated person resembling an infant are unique to Olmec art, most examples coming from funerary and ritual deposits from the central Mexican highland states of Morelos and Puebla. Most were intentionally broken prior to burial in ritual caches. Some examples might have functioned as surrogates for infant sacrifices or, when found in adult burials, as symbols of spiritual rebirth. Others have symbolic icons carved, incised, or painted on their heads or backs. The incised and painted emblem on the top and rear of this figure's head has been associated with

the god of springtime and regeneration.[1] The motif also resembles the "four-dots-and-bar" icon, interpreted as a diagram of Olmec cosmology.[2] Yet it is most similar to the iconographic complex that distinguishes the Olmec maize god, including this deity's essential cleft-head.[3]

Many of these figures are in a seated position with outstretched legs, gesturing with an upraised arm or similar measured body position. Depicted with a slightly open mouth and upraised eyes and lacking genitalia, these enigmatic figures seem to reject the adult, human condition and embrace the spirit form. The seated position and limited repertoire of gestures suggest disciplined meditative exercises that would assist the shaman in his/her spiritual journey.[4] Non-sexed figures of adults in contorted positions are relatively common in Olmec art, from monumental versions carved in stone to

diminutive examples modeled in clay. They may depict postures taken by shamans, whether actual or metaphorical, for the rigors of spiritual transformation. The practice survives today among Huichol shamanic celebrants in northern Mexico.[5]

Notes

1. Washington 1996, 170, no. 9 (B. de la Fuente).

2. Joralemon 1974, 33, 37. See also Princeton 1995, 153–54, no. 25 (F. Kent Reilly).

3. Fields and Reents-Budet 2005, 21–27; Taube 2005, 102.

4. Tate 1995, 57–58. See also Princeton 1995, 128–29.

5. Reilly and Tate 1995.

11, 12. TWO BOWLS WITH INCISED MOTIFS

Olmec, Central Highlands, Mexico
Early to Middle Formative Periods, 1200–600 BCE
Burnished and incised earthenware
No. 11 (TL.2009.20.269): 5.1 × 15.2 × 6.9 cm
No. 12 (TL.2009.20.270): 10.5 × 23.6 × 15.2 cm

The brown color and elongated, curvilinear form of these two bowls recall that of gourds, the most common food-service vessel in Mesoamerica. To this day, gourds remain an important household item as well as the preferred container for ceremonial offerings, from those for curing the sick to Catholic rites of veneration. Throughout Mexico, Belize, and Guatemala today, guests are honored by being served a chocolate beverage in a gourd drinking cup, a practice reaching back at least to 1600 BCE.[1]

These bowls' graceful curvature is accentuated by the burnish lines that follow the vessels' contours. In place of the gourds' stems, the artist incised geometric motifs that have symbolic associations. The four short, arched lines on no. 12 recall the gum line of the jaguar and the Olmec dragon, which symbolizes the surface of the earth.[2] Radiating from this important motif are parallel lines that imply the gourd's natural flutes. It is reported that the bowls were found together, one inside the other, and thus imply a formal pair.

Notes

1. San Francisco 2010, 132 (M. del Carmen Rodríguez and P. Ortíz Ceballos).
2. Reilly 1995, 121.

These two ceramic sculptures illustrate the stylistic differences between Formative Period works made in Mexico's central highlands and those from the western state of Guerrero. The head illustrates the typical Olmec-style fleshy face with facial features clustered together. The eyes are markedly slanted and slightly crossed, with pupils indicated by a sharp punctate in the clay. The well-defined horizontal ridge across the forehead may depict intentional binding of the cranium to achieve a specific head form for reasons of beauty or ideology, a practice found throughout ancient Mesoamerica. Although this figure's body is missing, the head's upraised position recalls that of the hollow, infantile sculptures (see no. 10).

The standing figure may be a female, suggested by the graceful curve of the torso indicating her waistline, the thickened thighs, and the small, erect breasts. She stands rigid with left arm raised and right arm slightly outstretched, recalling the ritual poses of the larger hollow, seated figures (see no. 10). The artist emphasized the upraised, bulbous head, slanted eyes and half-opened mouth, all conforming to a codified repertoire of Olmec figural features that represent ritual behavior and spiritual beliefs.

13. HEAD FROM A FIGURE

Olmec, Guerrero, Mexico

Early Formative Period, 1200–900 BCE

Earthenware

12.1 × 8.9 × 8.9 cm

TL.2009.20.185

14. STANDING FIGURE

Olmec (Pilli-type), Central Highlands, Mexico

Archaic to Early Formative Periods,

1500–1000 BCE

Earthenware

18.3 × 10.7 × 3.5 cm

TL.2009.20.262

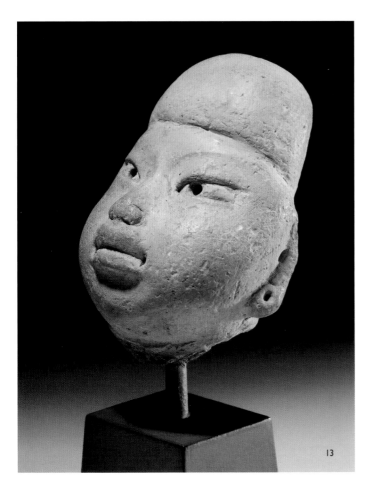

13

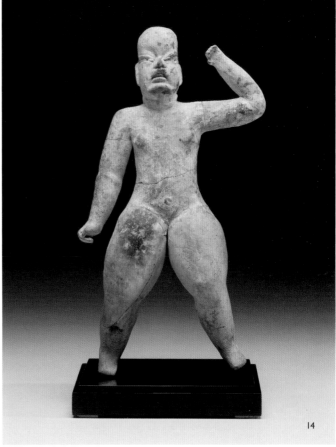

14

15. BALLPLAYER FIGURE

Olmec, Gulf Coast Lowlands, Mexico
Middle Formative Period, 900–600 BCE
Jadeite
9 × 4.2 × 2.5 cm
TL.2009.20.228

The identification of this figure as a ball-player rests on the characteristically wide belt, or "yoke," around his waist.[1] He carries a rectangular item in his left arm, and his right hand clutches a cylindrical object, per-haps a ball-striking implement used in some versions of the game. Underneath the yoke, the player wears a loincloth and hip wrap, which falls below his buttocks. His head is tied with a wide knotted strap, and his large disk pendant resembles the divining mirror seen on other Olmec-style figurines.[2]

The Mesoamerican ballgame was a mul-tifaceted event. It was played as sport, and among the sixteenth-century Aztecs, there was much betting and revelry. The game also was a ritualized reflection of cosmic forces, a ceremonial petition for fertility, and a rite during which the supernatural realm was made manifest.[3] The ballgame has very ancient origins in Mesoamerica; the earliest known ballcourt, dating to about 1400 BCE, was found at Paso de la Amada in Chiapas, Mexico.[4]

Notes

1. San Francisco 2010, 232 (V. M. Fields). See also Scarborough and Wilcox 1991; J. Scott 2001.

2. San Francisco 2010, 158–59, pl. 71.

3. Bradley 2001.

4. Hill 1999.

16, 17. TRIPOD VESSELS

Teotihuacan style, Mexico

Earthenware, red pigment

No. 16 (TL.2009.20.98): height 7.2 cm, diameter 7.1 cm

No. 17 (TL.2009.20.99): height 7.4 cm, diameter 7.1 cm

18. WARRIOR FACE (INCENSE BURNER FRAGMENT)

Teotihuacan, Mexico

Middle Classic Period, 400–650 CE

Earthenware, post-fire pigment

21.8 × 25 × 4.3 cm

TL.2009.20.248

The tripod dish is a vessel form intimately associated with Teotihuacan, the most powerful political force during Mesoamerica's Classic Period (100–900 CE). Expanding from its capital, named "Teotihuacan" (Place of the Gods) by the Aztecs nearly a thousand years later, Teotihuacan's influence spread east and west from coast to coast in central Mexico and south into the Maya regions of Guatemala and Honduras, reaching into northwestern Costa Rica in Central America.

Each of these paired tiny tripod dishes is decorated with a procession of Teotihuacan warriors, carrying the spear thrower and long darts of its military orders. Their costumes include the double-ring eye or head adornment (no. 16) and butterfly headdress (no. 17) often worn by members of the martial forces. The same headdress, typically associated with Teotihuacan's elite combatants,

is depicted frontally on this incense burner (no. 18). There are iconographic anomalies on both vessels, however, notable in such elements as the headdresses and large emblems separating the figures, which bring into question the origin of the incised narrative.

Technical Commentary

Both of these miniature tripod vessels are similarly made and in pristine condition. Hand formed and thin walled, each is covered with a dark brown, burnished slip colored with manganese and iron. After the slip was applied but before firing, the outer surfaces were carved and incised, leaving the design in relief. Three separately made feet, either mold-made or stamped, were also added to the bottom of the vessel before firing. After firing, a red, iron-based paint was used to highlight the incised decoration.[1] The incision work on no. 17 is more deeply and forcefully rendered than in no. 16 and may represent a different hand. The similarity in slip and pigment analyses nonetheless indicates that the two vessels were certainly made at the same time and place. The vessels are undergoing further analysis, including thermoluminescence dating (JL).

Note

1. XRF analysis identified high levels of iron, indicating the use of an iron-based pigment. The use of red iron oxide (Fe_2O_3) as a pigment to decorate stuccoed tripod vessels from Teotihuacan is documented in Fletcher 2002, 141, table 2.

19. INCENSE BURNER

Maya, Pacific Coast, Guatemala
Middle Classic Period, 350–500 CE
Earthenware, post-fire paint
41.2 × 48.7 × 29.6 cm
TL.2009.20.192

This elaborate incense burner unites a Teotihuacan ritual object with a Maya mythological narrative. It features a supernatural being, perhaps a deified ancestor, emerging from a large shell that symbolizes the entrance into the watery underworld. The figure grasps the edge of the shell with his left hand to aid his emergence into the human realm. He wears a three-strand necklace of round beads; a smaller version of the shell from which he rises dangles on his chest. His upper arms, too, are adorned with one shell each, and double strands of small beads decorate each wrist. The yellow paint of his jewelry may indicate that all were fashioned from shell.

The narrative lid sits atop a base embellished with the trapezoidal nose adornment typical of the Teotihuacan elite, and large earflares are attached to each flange at the base's sides. Together these imply an adorned head, perhaps functioning as a personified representation of the earth. The base held the burning coals and incense, the smoke rising into the lid and issuing from large holes at either end of the shell. A thermoluminescence (TL) date analysis of three samples from this incense burner reveals it has been fired within the last 100 years.[1] This could be the result of refiring the object to mask restoration work or it could indicate a piece made recently.

Note

1. TL analysis performed by Oxford Authentication Ltd., Oxfordshire, England.

One element of the strategic brilliance of the Mexica political machine was its incorporation of conquered towns' local deities into the imperial pantheon, its two primary gods being their patron deity Huitzilopochtli and Tlaloc, the deity of rain. By integrating local ideologies with that of the Mexica state, the Aztecs assimilated disparate groups into their expanding social, political, and economic structures. Such cultural absorbtion is attested in many artworks, foremost being the myriad sculptures of Tlaloc produced throughout Mexico. These portrayals range from the finest artistry to relatively crude carvings, the latter often found in village contexts or at ritual springs or mountain shrines associated with the deity. Many were

covered with stucco and painted black, the color of thunder clouds that form around mountain tops. This example features iconography typically associated with the deity: a wide headband, a crownlike headdress composed of long strips of paper, a folded paper fan behind the head (only a fragment survives on the proper right side of the sculpture), circular eye rings, and a mustachelike upper lip.[1] The Mexica particularly associated Tlaloc with the fertility gods of the previous civilizations of Mesoamerica such as Teotihuacan.[2]

Most Aztec stone sculptures depict female deities, especially the so-called Goddess with Temple Headdress, a maize deity.[3] This example (no. 21) typifies the smaller

20. TLALOC SCULPTURE

Mexica (Aztec), Mexico
Late Postclassic Period, 1400–1521 CE
Volcanic stone, traces of white stucco and red, blue, and green pigments
50.2 × 28.8 × 27.5 cm
TL.2009.20.201

21. MAIZE DEITY

Mexica (Aztec), Mexico
Late Postclassic Period, 1400–1521 CE
Volcanic stone, traces of red pigment
54.9 × 19.6 × 14.6 cm
TL.2009.20.199

20

21

portrayals carved in simple formats that are found outside the Mexica capital Teno-chtitlan (present-day Mexico City). The abundance of such figures and their less-finished carving suggest a kind of mass production intended for local shrines rather than for the majestic temples of Tenochtit-lan, whose sculptures often are of the highest quality and aesthetic expression. This god-dess figure retains the rectangular form of the stone block from which she was carved, recalling the sculptural traditions of the eastern Gulf Coast region rather than the more volumetric style of the central high-lands. Details of the headdress identify the figure as a maize goddess, perhaps an aspect of Chicomecóatl. Her upraised hands hold two cylindrical forms—probably maize cobs as seen in sculptures of Xilonen, the deity of young maize.[4] The iconography, whether intended to represent one or the other deity, is associated with fertility and fruitfulness.

Technical Commentary

The porous gray volcanic stone, with large quartz like inclusions, from which the fig-ure of Tlaloc (no. 20) was carved has not been identified; volcanic stones with similar characteristics, such as scoria and basalt, are known to have been used by the Aztecs for sculptural works. The figure is carved fully in the round with a solid flat top and bottom. The entire surface was originally covered with a layer of fine white stucco and painted.[5] Traces of red, green, and blue pig-ments remain in the carved recesses (fig. 1). The presence of layers of stucco sandwich-ing a green pigment layer in a protected area on the figure's right indicates that the object was whitewashed and repainted at least twice (JA).

Notes

1. New York 2004, 99.

2. Pasztory 1983, 222.

3. Ibid. 1983, 218–19.

4. Ibid. 1983, pls. 180–81.

5. Fourier-transform infrared spectroscopy performed at the Walters Art Museum by Glenn Gates identified calcium carbonate ($CaCO_3$) as the major component of the white stucco.

Fig. 1 (left). Arrows indicate the location of the blue-green, red, and green pigments in remnants of stucco on no. 20. The green pigment layer is sandwiched between two layers of stucco.

Fig. 2 (right). Side view of Tlaloc figure, no. 20

22. TWO TRIPOD DISHES

Mixteca-Puebla (Eastern Nahua), Mexico
Late Postclassic Period, 1450–1521 CE
Earthenware, burnished slip paint
Overall: 20.5 × 18.6 × 20.8 cm
TL.2009.20.239

The misnamed "lacquerware" is an artistic accomplishment of the Postclassic Period, having been developed in the Mixteca-Puebla region east and south of the Valley of Mexico. Aztec nobility preferred this hard and shiny-surfaced, slip-painted earthenware for their food-service vessels, importing large quantities from Cholula and other cities in the region. Mixteca-Puebla pottery is renowned for its well-controlled polychromy and lively decorative programs that depict symbolic elements or entire scenes from religious myths.

This pair of tripod dishes combines the polychrome painting of the Mixteca-Puebla tradition with the controlled decorative approach that typifies Postclassic pottery from central Mexico. The painter blended the all-important Mesoamerican stepped-fret motif as the primary decorative element with more simplified rectangles of cross-hatched design. The exterior bottom of each vessel displays a binary image of a feathered saurian head, perhaps an allusion to the culture hero and deity Quetzalcóatl. The tall, step-form tripods recall the cut-out tripod supports typical of fifth-century Teotihuacan pottery. It is likely that the Mixteca-Puebla and Aztec pottery artists adopted this time-honored form to associate their specialized ritual wares with the ancient majesty of Teotihuacan, the "City of the Gods." The interior bottom of each dish contains three bands of raised geometric elements. It is unknown whether these vessels were used to grind or abrade a foodstuff or other organic substance or whether they served a solely ritual, service function.

23

23. MASK

Mexica (Aztec), Mexico
Late Postclassic Period, 1400–1521 CE
Wood, white ground with traces of black and red paint
17.2 × 14 × 7.2 cm
2009.20.1

24. MASK

Mexica (Aztec), Mexico
Late Postclassic Period, 1400–1521 CE
Earthenware
13.5 × 8.6 × 3.8 cm
TL.2009.20.121

Throughout Mesoamerica, the wearing of masks was central to the performance of religious rituals and reenactments of myths and history. The face is the center of identity, and by changing one's face, a person can transcend the bounds of self, social expectations, and even earthly limitations. In this transformed state, the human becomes the god, supernatural being or mythic hero portrayed.[1] Masks of skeletal heads, whether human (no. 23) or animal (no. 24), are relatively common, for death played a central role in Mexica religion. Death was one of the twenty daysigns of the Mexican calendar, indicating its essential place in the natural cycle of the cosmos.

Death also was directly connected to the concept of regeneration and resurrection, which was a basic principle in Aztec religious philosophy.[2] A key Mexica myth recounts the journey of Ehecatl, a wind god who was an aspect of Quetzalcóatl ("Feathered Serpent"), a powerful Mesoamerican deity. Ehecatl travels to Mictlán, the land of the dead, where he retrieves the bones of long-dead ancestors. He grinds their bones and mixes the powder with his blood, offered in sacrifice. With this potent mixture, the god formed the new race of humans who, according to Mexica cosmology, inhabit the present fifth age of Creation. Thus, death and rebirth are intimately connected in Aztec thought and religious practice.

Both masks represent the concept of life generated from death with visages animated by lively eyes and painted skin. Both were probably worn during rituals, covering the performer's face or attached to an elaborate, full-head mask. Either type transforms the person into a new being that symbolizes the pan-Mesoamerican belief in life springing from death as a natural, and inevitable, process of the mystical universe.

Technical Commentary

No. 23 is carved from a single piece of wood. The white paint (composed largely of gypsum) that once entirely covered both the mask's interior and exterior served as a ground for painted decoration.[3] Remnants of designs painted in black and dark red are visible (fig. 1). Red paint was used on the ears and forehead, and to create thin, vertical parallel lines and circle patterns on the lower cheeks. The eyeballs and lines on the teeth are executed in black. Additionally, large areas under the nose and chin were painted solid black.

The mask was broken in half vertically to the left of the nose and repaired (JA).

Notes

1. Markman and Markman 1989, xix–xxi, 3.
2. M. Miller and Taube 1993, 74, 141, 177–78.
3. The white material was identified as gypsum through Fourier-transform infrared spectroscopy performed at the Walters Art Museum.

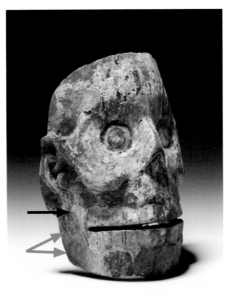

Fig. 1. The black arrow indicates an area where red pigment was used to create thin, vertical lines. The red arrows indicate red circles. Black pigment, more clearly visible than the red, is present in the eyes, under the nose, and on the teeth and chin.

25. FEMALE BALLPLAYER FIGURINE

Huastec, northern Veracruz, Mexico
Classic Period, 300–800 CE
Earthenware
35.2 × 9.6 × 4.6 cm
TL.2009.20.165

26. FEMALE BALLPLAYER FIGURINE

Huastec, northern Veracruz, Mexico
Late Classic to Early Postclassic Periods,
800–1300 CE
Earthenware, bituminous black paint
39.4 × 17.8 × 7 cm
TL.2009.20.162

The ritual ballgame was especially popular among many societies of the Gulf Coast, the Classic Period site of El Tajín being famous for its eleven formal ballcourts adorned with stone, stucco, and painted decoration. Ceramic and stone representations of ballplayers were produced in large numbers throughout Veracruz; the Huastecs of the north are well known for pottery figurines depicting these athlete-performers. Although most of the figurines portray males, female players are frequently represented in Huastec art, their production spanning at least six hundred years. These two impressive figures are excellent examples of the styles.

The Classic Period figurine (no. 25) wears the usual hip wrap ("yoke"), elbow pads, and knee protectors of Mesoamerican ballplayers.[1] She sports the head wrap and erect panache of feathers (portraying a diving bird) typically seen on other Huastec ballplayer figurines.[2] Her personal adornments include wide earflares, a choker necklace of spherical beads, and a longer necklace with three celtlike pendants; such jewelry was usually made of jadeite. Body paint or intentional scarification lines embellish her shoulders, another feature frequently seen on ballplayer portrayals.

The later figurine (no. 26) is identifiable as a ballplayer by the knee and elbow pads, although her bent arms cover the hips and obscure whatever hip wrap she may be wearing. Instead, a simple pubic cover is visible between her hands. Her elaborate head gear recalls the fanlike ritual headdress of the Postclassic Huastecs, connoting high status, rulership, and/or sacredness. The long groups of feathers and the trilobed element on her forehead constitute a later interpretation of the same diving bird headdress seen on the earlier figurine. Her body and mouth are adorned with seven painted three-pronged motifs resembling a waterbird's footprint. The meaning of this motif is unknown, although the practice of painting the body with symbolic motifs or glyphlike forms dates back at least to the Late Preclassic Period in the Huastec area.[3]

Notes

1. J. Scott 2001, 51–63.

2. Goldstein 1988, 39.

3. Ibid., 45, no. 4.

27. SEATED MALE FIGURE WITH INCENSE BURNER

Remojades or Nopiloa,

south-central Veracruz, Mexico

Late Classic Period, 600–900 CE

Earthenware

17.4 × 12.6 × 11.7 cm

TL.2009.20.222

The vibrant naturalism of this exceptionally fine ceramic sculpture belies its ritual meaning. The seated man looks forward and slightly to the right, his concentrated gaze underscoring his dignity and the seriousness of the moment. He lightly grasps a large incense burner by its coiled handles, seemingly ready to transport the container of burning coals and incense.

This sculpture is especially intriguing for its detailed rendering of elements of costume and textile patterns. The figure sports a doubled head wrap of highly decorated cloth, its raised motifs likely depicting brocade or embroidery. Both decorative techniques are typical of fine native dress throughout present-day Veracruz. The figure's upper torso is covered by a short cape that may be made of striped material or strips of cloth sewn together. Large ropes of twisted fiber adorn his shoulders, and a larger rope encircles his neck. This latter accouterment may identify the figure as a captive nobleman destined for sacrifice. His exceptionally large earflares indicate high status, and intentional scarification beautifies his face and chest. The naturalistic details of this figure and his dress, as well the nobleman's intense countenance, give this small-scale figurine a monumental presence.

28. FEMALE FIGURE

Nopiloa, south-central Veracruz,

Gulf Coast, Mexico

Late Classic Period, 600–900 CE

Earthenware, traces of white ground or paint

28.4 × 23.3 × 10 cm

2009.20.27

Exquisitely molded and modeled, this splendid rendering of a woman with a basket typifies the detailed ceramic sculptures of Classic Period Veracruz. The naturalistic depiction of soft, pliable cloth in the rigid medium of fired clay attests to the artist's command of the medium. The lady's elaborate headdress is composed of a wide, plain piece of cloth wrapped around her head bound with head bands of oval beads and strips of cloth. Her body is draped in a sleeved tunic that floats on top of her long wrap skirt.

She is adorned with a single-strand necklace of rounded beads and a central rectangular pendant, with smaller versions encircling each wrist. The necklace is tied at the back of her neck, its four thin tie-ends terminating in oblong beads. The figure's ornate earrings represent sectioned conch shells. The sectioned conch shell is the "wind jewel" or *ehecailacacozcatl*, an identifying symbol of Quetzalcóatl, the god of rain, wind, and war during the Classic Period. This deity was particularly associated with the cultures of the Gulf Coast.[1] During Postclassic times, Quetzalcóatl was closely connected with the pilgrimage center of Cholula, located on the passage between coastal Veracruz and the Valley of Mexico, where he was the patron of rulers and associated with priests and merchants as well.

On her right shoulder this Nopiloa lady balances a flat-bottomed basket with a double-strap handle, recalling the typical carrying baskets used by women in Mexican markets today. The basket contains a pile of hand-made cigars and an unidentified rectangular folded item. Her fine dress and sophisticated jewelry suggest that she is more than a commonplace market girl.

Note

1. M. Miller and Taube 1993, 141–42.

29. MALE FIGURE

Río Blanco area, southern Veracruz, Gulf Coast, Mexico
Late Classic Period, 600–900 CE[1]
Earthenware, black paint
108.5 × 50.9 × 30.3 cm
TL.2009.20.198

The sculptural style of this male figue is known as El Zapotal or Upper Remojades I, named for archaeological sites in the Río Blanco coastal plain of Veracruz where artifacts of this type have been found.[2] At El Zapotal, large-scale, hollow ceramics depicting humans, deity impersonators, and animals, as well as ritual paraphernalia such as incense burners with decorated lids were found buried inside architectural mounds. Some were grouped together, their arrangement suggesting a vignette of ritual behavior or ideology preserved in sculpted clay. Most were intentionally broken before burial.

The figure's jaguar helmet-headdress identifies him as a warrior. He may be a vanquished combatant, implied by the ropelike element around his neck, the thinner ropes encircling his torso, and his nudity. Throughout Mesoamerica, captured warriors were often denuded during victory celebrations and subsequent sacrificial rites. His nearly closed eyes and slightly opened mouth may signify a trancelike state or perhaps death.[3] The turtle carapace drum in his right hand connotes a ritual performance.

The figure appears to wear the flayed skin of a sacrificial victim, intimated by the "sleeves" on each arm (note the end of the skin at each wrist). The donning of flayed skin was part of the rituals associated with the god Xipe Totec.[4] This deity, particularly venerated among peoples of the Gulf Coast, is associated with the miracle of agricultural renewal each springtime. In the sixteenth century, the god's festival occurred during March, when farmers began preparing their fields for planting. Just as the flayed skin would rot on the body of the ritual participant, eventually revealing the young, vital warrior within, so too the planted seed's husk rots and the new, vigorous sprout emerges.

Notes

1. Thermoluminescence analysis, performed by Oxford Authentication Ltd., Oxfordshire, England, showed that two samples, taken from the back of the

30. FIGURAL URN

Zapotec, Oaxaca, Mexico

Late Classic Period, Monte Albán IIIb,

450–650 CE

Earthenware

68.8 × 42.3 × 32 cm

TL.2009.20.293

Large, figural urn effigies are unique to Zapotec sculptural traditions of the Late Preclassic and Classic periods. During Classic times, their forms and iconographic programs became institutionalized to such an extent that individual types can be identified and their symbolic meanings discerned. Most portray persons dressed as specific gods, especially the rain deity Cociyo and the maize god Pitao Cozobi.[1] They are found in building caches, usually as single offerings, or more frequently in tombs, often accompanied by a number of smaller "attendant" figural urns (see nos. 31, 32). No evidence of smoke or carbon has been found inside the cylindrical containers at the figures' back, belying their interpretation as incense burners. In a few instances, the containers were found to hold obsidian blades, jadeite adornments, and the remains of organic materials, all of which likely represent offerings and ritual items from the moment of internment or perhaps later veneration rites conducted in the tomb.

This commanding figure represents an impersonator of the maize god. The large size of the urn suggests that it was a tomb's main figure and, as such, may have symbolized a sacred ancestor of the tomb's occupant.[2] His headdress features the hieroglyph *Lape* (drop, rain), which is the nineteenth day in the Zapotec calendar. Its iconographic origin is a bundle of maize leaves. The blending of maize god and rain imagery is mirrored in the figure's large, elaborate earflares, which allude to the rain god Cociyo. The trilobed element

emerging from the earflares usually is found in the basal panels of other urns along with the image of an alligator. In all instances, the main figure is Cociyo.[3] The ornate pendant covering the impersonator's chest is the maize god's pectoral glyph, which signifies the four-sided maize field. The presence of the maize god's chest ornament and the rain-maize headdress glyph unambiguously identifies the deity impersonated by this figure as the maize god and not Cociyo.[4]

Technical Commentary

This figural urn has been broken and reassembled from numerous pieces (see p. 195, fig. 14). Portions of the legs, hands, arms,

Fig. 1. The proper right earflare and the pectoral are carved from clay slabs rather than mold made.

and headdress have been restored. The object was constructed as a columnar vessel with a flat, solid bottom that serves as the figure's torso, head, and headdress, to which were added the figure's hollow legs and arms, pectoral, ears, and earflares. The headdress, earflares, and pectoral are carved slabs of clay rather than mold-made elements (fig. 1).[5] No traces of post-fire paint have been identified; alterations in the vessel's surface are the result of previous restorations.[6]

The object was sampled in four areas for thermoluminescence dating; all samples were reported to be last fired 1,200–1,900 years ago, falling within the proposed date range of manufacture (450–650 CE) (JA).[7]

Notes

1. New York 1970, 190–92, 197.

2. Urcid 2005, 64.

3. Ibid., 62 n. 53.

4. Ibid., 60. See also Sellen 2003.

5. Zapotec urns have been found to be low-fired ceramics, assembled before firing from numerous components and made using hand modeling and carving techniques, as well as press-molded elements. Alderson 2002, 146.

6. Almost all Zapotec urns in museums in Mexico, the United States, and in the literature have traces of post-fire paint. A few examples have full polychromy, but most do not appear to have been elaborately painted. Ibid.

7. Thermoluminescence analysis was performed by Oxford Authentication Ltd., Oxfordshire, England.

31

32

31, 32. FIGURAL URNS

Zapotec, Oaxaca, Mexico

Late Classic Period,

Monte Albán IIIb, 450–650 CE[1]

Earthenware, post-fire paint (red)

No. 31 (2009.20.21): 39 × 27.4 × 23.9 cm

No. 32 (2009.20.22): 40.1 × 25.5 × 25.9 cm

These two urns likely were part of a larger grouping of similarly small figural sculptures surrounding a large one that created a ceramic narrative tableau like that of the famous royal Zapotec Tomb 104 at Monte Albán, Oaxaca.[2] These two urns portray impersonators of the Zapotec rain god Cociyo, here wearing a full face mask rather than the more common buccal (lower face, or mouth) mask. The figures' deeply striated hair was originally painted with what may have been an orange-hued pigment. In other renderings of these rain god impersonators, the hair is painted yellow, signifying maize silk.[3] The same hairstyle, although unpainted, is also found on the large urn portraying the maize god (see no. 30). These two small figures wear a curious pectoral suspended by a thick twined rope around their necks. It may depict a folded piece of paper, cloth, or similarly malleable material tied with a braided band.

In Zapotec tombs documented by archaeologists, small rain god urns have been found in sets of four placed around a large urn portraying the maize god/progenitor-ancestor.[4] Such an arrangement replicates the five-fold Mesoamerican universe (the four cardinal directions plus the center), with the maize god/progenitor-ancestor as the *axis mundi* at the world's center, with its four sides defined by rain gods.[5] The maize god at the center symbolizes the sacred mountain of origin from which all life emerged onto earth. The overarching narrative of these urn tableaux recounts the origin of the Zapotec people from maize and the seminal roles of the maize god Pitao Cozobi and the rain god Cociyo in Creation.

Notes

1. Thermoluminescence analysis performed by Oxford Authentication Ltd., Oxfordshire, England, showed that six samples, three taken from each urn, were last fired between 1,200 and 1,900 years ago. This date range is consistent with the proposed date of manufacture (450–650 CE).

2. Caso and Bernal 1952. See also Urcid 2005, fig. 4.4.

3. Urcid 2005, 61, fig. 4.12.

4. Ibid., fig. 4.4.

5. Freidel, Schele, and Parker 1993, 59–122. See also Thompson 1970; Heyden 1981.

33. SEATED FIGURE

Colima, Mexico
Comala phase, 100 BCE–300 CE
Earthenware, burnished slip in
red and light brown
25.2 × 18 × 21.5 cm
2009.20.16

The valleys of the Río Armería and Río
Coahuayana, which drain the mountains of
the modern Mexican state of Colima, nur-
tured the development of a robust culture.
Although the peoples' names and languages
are lost to time, their vitality is preserved in
remarkable ceramic sculptures and a pottery
vessel tradition that are unique in Mesoamerica. Yet these artworks also incorporate
a variety of features found among many
Mexican societies, thereby indicating ancient
Colima's membership in the greater Mesoamerican community.

Colima's hollow figural art, characterized by its monochrome orange-red or deep
red slip palette, is one of the most unified
artistic statements of Mesoamerica. The
surfaces were highly burnished to achieve
a bright shine, interrupted only by black
manganese staining resulting from a natural
corrosive process. Here the sculptor draws
attention away from the engaging figure by
highlighting the vessel's orifice with deep
red slip paint. The sculptor's mastery of the
human form is seen in the adept rendering
of the twist of the back as the figure leans
forward on his bent knee. The acuteness of
the twist, however, may also depict a skeletal
defect. The figure's gesture—right hand held
to the chest—is a pan-Mesoamerican sign of
deference.

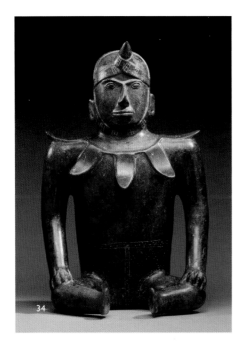

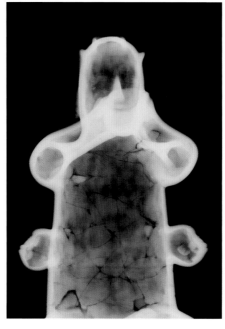

Fig. 1. Digital x-ray image of no. 35, showing multiple breaks, some small fills, and the fairly even wall thickness of the hollow figure

34. SEATED MALE

Colima, Mexico

Comala phase, 100 BCE–300 CE

Earthenware, burnished slip paint in red and light brown, with incising

43.4 × 29.1 × 23.2 cm

2009.20.13

35. SEATED MALE WITH TROPHY HEADS

Colima, Mexico

Comala phase, 100 BCE–300 CE

Earthenware, burnished slip paint in red and light brown, incising

43.6 × 25 × 27.2 cm

2009.20.10

These figures-as-vessel both feature a seated male of commanding presence. The sculptor of no. 35 painted the jar's orifice and the man's arms with dark red slip to contrast with the piece's otherwise orange-red coloration. The figure's loins are covered by the typical male hip cloth, indicated here by incised lines. He holds a gourd-shaped bowl to his mouth ready to drink its contents,

perhaps a chocolate or alcoholic beverage. A helmetlike head covering includes an arched element above each ear and a hornlike protrusion at the front.

The dark red-slipped figure (no. 34) portrays a man with confident visage in a straightforward, commanding seated position. His hornlike protrusion is tied to his head with embellished (embroidered?) cloth straps, and his hip wrap is equally well decorated. He also sports an elaborate necklace of large shells.

The one sculpture (no. 35) might portray a warrior, implied by the two trophy heads slung across his chest and hanging at his sides.[1] The horned element atop both figures' foreheads suggests other interpretations, particularly that of a shaman and his supernatural horn. The shaman would use the horn to battle malevolent spiritual forces, the horn also symbolizing his *tonalli* (vital essence and spirit power).[2] An alternative interpretation views the hornlike element as a symbol of social hierarchy and rulership, sacrifice, and cosmic geography and the earth's fertility.[3] It represents a prong cut from a conch shell that throughout

Mesoamerica was associated with rituals of sacrifice and warfare, and also expressed political rank. As such, both figures may be understood as portraying a person of social and political authority based on religious ideology.[4] This latter interpretation is supported by the feasting implication of the figure holding the gourd-shaped bowl, feasting being an integral part of elite activities throughout the ancient Americas (see the following entries).[5]

Notes

1. This sculpture is nearly identical to one in the Museum für Volkerkunde in Berlin. See Townsend 1998b, 116, fig. 10.

2. Furst 1998, 180–82.

3. Graham 1998, 195–96.

4. Ibid., 198, 200

5. Butterwick 1998, 90.

35

36

36. SEATED FEMALE FIGURE

Coahuayana, Colima-Michoacán, Mexico
100 BCE–300 CE
Earthenware, burnished red slip paint with resist (?) designs in black
49.5 × 30.5 × 24.8 cm
2009.20.53

37. FIGURE WITH LARGE BOWL

Colima, Mexico
200 BCE–300 CE
Earthenware, slip paint
26.9 × 24 × 30.9 cm
2009.20.18

38. FIGURE WITH LARGE BOWL

Colima, Mexico
200 BCE–300 CE
Earthenware
18 × 22.6 × 26.6 cm
2009.20.20

The Coahuayana River Valley was home to many large villages and towns, and their artists produced a distinctive local version of the large, hollow tomb figure.[1] Coahuayana figural art is characterized by elegant renderings of persons of authority. Most portrayals lack individuality and instead serve as sculptural representations of social position or political rank.[2] This seated female's serene countenance, shoulder scarification patterns, necklace, and pierced ears denote a person of high status. The artist accentuated the figure with red slip, enhancing her hair, forearms, and legs below the knee. Her identification as a person of authority is further indicated by her sitting on a four-legged stool or bench; this type of seating was closely associated with elevated status throughout the ancient Americas.[3] She raises a small dish in her right hand as if proffering its contents to unseen persons, perhaps participants in an aristocratic feasting event.

The feast was a critical part of sociopolitics throughout ancient Mesoamerica.[4] It was a forum for cementing alliances, forging new relationships, and strengthening obligations of reciprocity; it also served as a mechanism for redistributing goods, which enhanced the host's prestige and stimulated production and use. The two seated figures (nos. 37, 38) are not only excellent technical achievements but also compelling artworks whose narrative underscores the importance of the feast to West Mexican social politics. These figures may be identified as attendants at a feast, each cradling a large vessel, or perhaps a basket in the case of the wide-handled vessel of no. 38. The containers would have held such foods as savory tamales, *atole* (maize cereal), or any number of other foods that during ancient, Colonial, and modern times constituted appropriate formal banquet fare.

Notes

1. Kan 1970, 25.

2. Pickering and Cabrero 1998, 83.

3. Butterwick 1998, 96.

4. Reents-Budet 2000; Townsend 1998a, 25–26.

37

38

39. SEATED FIGURE

Colima, Mexico
100 BCE–300 CE
Burnished earthenware
42 × 19.5 × 22.2 cm
TL.2009.20.212

This figure shares stylistic features with pottery sculptures from Nayarit as well as the Coahuayana figures of southern Colima and the adjacent Tuxcacuesco-Ortíces area. The tradition is distinguished by stylized depictions of persons of authority. The body is reduced to simple shapes, and body parts are elongated into forms that bear little resemblance to physical reality. Rather, they constitute artistically sophisticated allusions to the human body, seen here especially in the arms and back. All portrayals lack individuality, serving instead as sculptural representations of social position or political rank.[1] This figure's high status is indicated by his sitting on a low bench, the formalized seat of authority throughout Mesoamerica.

His multiple earrings, well-formed head wrap, and composed demeanor support his identification as a person of elevated position.

West Mexico's shaft tombs were filled with ceramic sculptures that represent a variety of social and political personages, including warriors, ballplayers, feasting individuals, and members of the ruling ranks seated on stools or benches. Each depiction might record important events or achievements in the life of the interred. This seated figure, then, might represent the moment of the tomb occupant's accession to high office.

Note

1. Pickering and Cabrero 1998, 83.

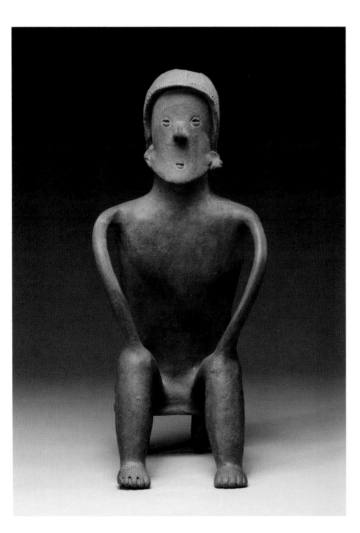

40. INCENSE BURNER STAND

Colima, Mexico

Early Postclassic Period, 900–1200 CE

Earthenware, white paint

44.7 × 27.6 × 27.8 cm

TL.2009.20.285

41. INCENSE BURNER STAND

Colima, Mexico

Early Postclassic Period, 900–1200 CE

Earthenware, white paint

23.9 × 21.5 × 23.5 cm

TL.2009.20.284

42. INCENSE BURNER STAND

Colima, Mexico

Early Postclassic Period, 900–1200 CE

Earthenware

31.4 × 19.8 × 20.7 cm

TL.2009.20.286

Large incense burner stands are a hallmark of the Postclassic period in Colima. The stands likely were placed on altars or the exteriors of temples, a low dish with burning coals and incense being placed either atop the columnar stand or underneath it; the smoke rose through the column and issued from openings in the face. The rounded eyes recall the Central Mexican rain deity Tlaloc, this distinctive representational style perhaps having been appropriated from Central Mexico and adapted by the peoples of Colima as part of socioeconomic interaction. During the Postclassic Period, West Mexican peoples increasingly were in contact with highland Mexico, trading marine resources (especially shells), coveted green stones and other lithic materials, and copper objects made in West Mexico.

The spikes and flanges on these three stands not only served to dissipate heat absorbed from the burning coals; they also may symbolize the spikes of the ceiba, the tallest tree in the Mesoamerican forest. Among the Maya and other Mesoamerican societies, the ceiba was the model for the World Tree at the center of the cosmos, which maintained the universe's tripartite structure (heavens, earth, and underworld). The ceiba-World Tree also provided a supernatural pathway for religious practioners' spiritual journeys among the three realms. The face on the thinner, dark-hued stand (no. 42) includes a zoomorphic figure draped over the nose bridge. This may be the origin, or at least the artistic inspiration, for similar images found on contemporary West Mexican performance masks.[1]

Note

1. Reents-Budet 2009, 55–91, figs. 12B, 35.

43. CONJOINED MAN AND WOMAN / CURING RITUAL NARRATIVE

Jalisco, Mexico
100 BCE–300 CE
Burnished earthenware
46.7 × 44.2 × 35 cm
TL.2009.20.149

Conjoined figures constitute an infrequent but not unknown narrative type of West Mexican tomb sculptures. Those from Colima include a family group (man, woman, child), a mother and child, or combat scenes.[1] Combat is mirrored in a warrior-and-captive piece from Jalisco,[2] and male-female pairs are found not only in Jalisco but especially in Nayarit contexts. Other conjoined figures depict a cheek-piercing rite in which two or more men and women participate.[3] Some double figures have been interpreted as portrayals of a marriage or otherwise affianced couple given that the man and woman touch or embrace and visually engage each other with what could be interpreted as a tender gaze of affection, as is seen in this sculpture.[4] However, the rendering of personal affection is rare in Mesoamerican art, and the few Classic Maya examples from Jaina Island are interpreted as symbolic renderings rather than depictions of interpersonal intimacy. And although the often published "marriage couple" pairs of similar-looking male and female figures from West Mexico may imply a local tradition for ceramic portrayals of devoted couples, these pairings have no basis in archaeological reality. Instead, they most likely constitute a fabricated grouping invented by tomb robbers and art dealers.[5]

A closer examination of this paired-figure artwork suggests an alternative interpretation as a healing ceremony by a shaman-curer and his patient. In myriad similar examples, one of the figures wears a curious panachelike or hornlike element atop his/her head, as seen here, which may identify the person as a shaman.[6] Other conjoined figures feature one member grasping a rattle, rasp, or drum.[7] These instruments are intimately associated with shamanic practice, and they are frequently integral to healing rituals among present-day shaman-curers in Mexico.[8] In other instances, one of the figures holds a small bowl, implying the ingestion of a curing potion.[9] The weight of the available evidence suggests that this exceptionally expressive and sensitive sculpture portrays a curing ceremony rather than an amorous couple.

The piece was extensively examined using x-radiography and thermoluminescence (TL), the latter for dating the last firing of the object. The research establishes that the piece has suffered major damage, with all appendages having been repaired. The x-radiography revealed that the sculpture is composed of two figures, but whether they were originally conjoined is difficult to determine because all points where the bodies touch have been repaired. These repairs probably were done at a different time than the manufacture of the piece; the composition of their clay is different from that of the majority of the piece. The joins of the necks strongly suggest the heads are in their original, intended position, which supports their being an authentic conjoined pair. The four TL date samples were taken from only one of the two clay bodies, this choice being by chance rather than intention as the joins were not visible on the object's surface when the samples were taken. All four TL samples indicate a production date of 100–250 CE.

Technical Commentary

This complicated ceramic pair is hollow formed with the exception of the arms, which are solid continuous coils of clay attached at the shoulders. Its reduction-fired black surface is intentionally burnished or left matt to highlight facial or decorative elements. Natural variability in the appearance of the fired surface is partially concealed by modern paint. Now heavily restored, the pair was broken and reconstituted from more than fifty fragments. X-radiography revealed a network of what appeared to be homogeneous, conjoined fragments without major amounts of added restoration (fig. 1). Due to the complexity of the figures and

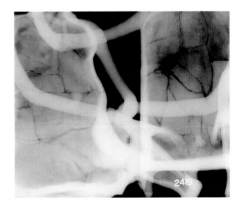

Fig. 1. X-radiograph: detail of torsos of both figures showing repair. The digital x-ray image was captured and viewed using GE Inspection Technologies' digital x-ray scanner and software.

the difficulty of interpreting the traditional x-radiograph, the pair was studied using computed tomography or CT.[10] CT images confirm that most areas where the two objects join are broken and repaired. Using "maximum intensity projection" imaging with CT, bright white spots highlight calcium-rich clays (fig. 2). Other areas of the figural group appear to have been made from a different clay.

Thermoluminescence analysis showed that four samples, two taken from each figure, were last fired between 1,500 and 2,400 years ago; these dates are consistent with the proposed date of manufacture between 100 BCE and 300 CE (JL).[11]

Notes

1. New York 1970, no. 91; Los Angeles 1970, no. 129; von Winning 1974, fig. 44.

2. Los Angeles 1970, nos. 76, 113.

3. Ibid., nos. 19, 22, 57.

4. Von Winning 1974, figs. 186, 187; Reents-Budet 2005, 53.

5. Pickering and Cabrero 1998, 86. For an opposing view, see Townsend 1998b, 128–30.

6. Furst 1998, 180–82. See also von Winning 1974, figs. 188, 193.

7. Von Winning 1974, figs. 190, 285, 287. See also Los Angeles 1970, nos. 14, 18, 77.

8. Furst 1998, 183–85.

9. Von Winning 1974, figs. 193, 285, 287. See also Los Angeles 1970, no. 14.

10. Computed tomography, a nondestructive technique thought to be especially useful in analyzing complicated figures such as the Jalisco group, was done at the University of Maryland Hospital by Dr. Barry Daly. At the time of publication, the study of the CT images was still in progress; details of the findings will be included in subsequent publications.

11. Thermoluminescence (TL) analysis was performed by Oxford Authentication Ltd., Oxfordshire, England. One drilled sample from the head and arm of each figure gave similar results. A sample taken from the edge of the stool was restoration material and could not be dated. All areas sampled for TL were taken from regions of fired clay body, which appear to be low in calcium on the evidence of recently available CT images.

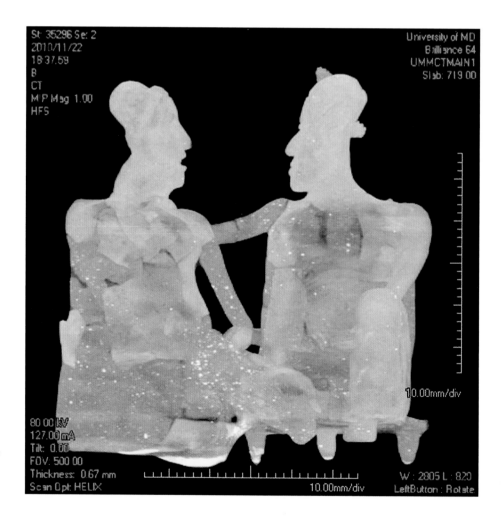

Fig. 2. CT scan equipped with "maximum intensity projection" showing calcium-rich inclusions in portions of the ceramic fragments

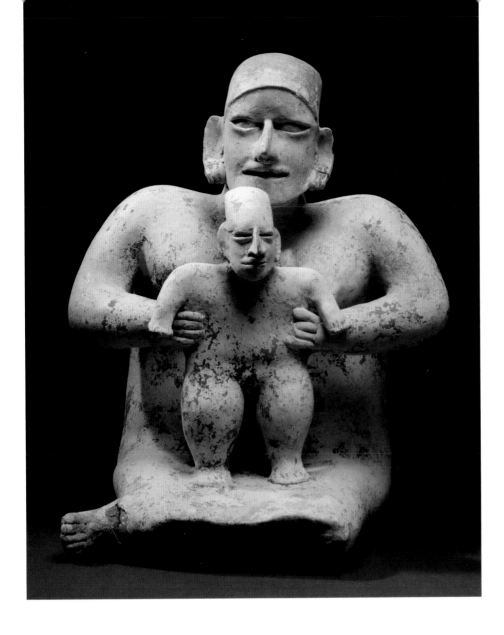

44. MOTHER AND CHILD

El Arenal, Jalisco, Mexico
100 BCE–200 CE
Earthenware, white slip with black and red paint
37.2 × 30.9 × 23.2 cm
2009.20.15

A mother proudly supports her male child who, with her help, stands securely on her lap. She sits in the proper position for women: legs folded to the side and concealed below her wrap skirt. This cream-slipped sculpture was made during the culmination of the shaft tomb tradition in West Mexico, when tombs were filled with spirited figural sculptures and decorated pottery vessels, and the bodies of the deceased were dressed in fine clothing and jewelry of shell and stone. The figures' cream-slipped surface and the restrained painting with which her dress is depicted are characteristic of an artistic substyle of the famous El Arenal Brown sculptural tradition of northern Jalisco.

Jalisco's pottery sculptors created a vast array of figures portraying all manner of social and political personages.[1] The figures are famous for the renderings of warriors brandishing shields and club-weapons and wearing helmets and armor of cotton batting. Others portray members of the ruling elite majestically standing with staff of office in hand. Shamans and healing rites were frequently depicted, as were individuals afflicted with diseases or congenital deformities. Portrayals of women were equally prominent, the majority featuring either their political or spiritual, shamanic powers or their magical ability to create life in the form of children. This sculpture is a particularly informal yet stately expression of the procreative power of women and their lifelong calling as nurturers.

Technical Commentary

X-radiography of this pair shows a hand-built form with clay walls of modulating thicknesses (fig. 1). Both the large and small figures are hollow and show evidence of slab construction.[2] Unlike other Jalisco ceramics examined, which have solid arms, those of this large figure are hollow. Partial overlap and pinching in of the clay walls just beneath the shoulders suggest that the shoulders were initially constructed as closed forms. Before the clay was fully dry, the shoulder socket was opened and premade arms were attached. Thickened areas around the eyes suggest that slabs of clay were added to the back of opened slots to create the orbs (fig. 2).

An internal mass of dense material is visible in the bottom of the torso and legs; the exact nature of this mass is not fully understood, but similar internal masses have been observed in other West Mexican ceramics in the collection.[3] These may be remnants of an internal core that facilitated the building of these complex hollow forms or added as a counterweight of some sort. The gray-bodied earthenware is covered with a white unburnished slip.[4] Small amounts of black and red paint were used to highlight facial features (JL).

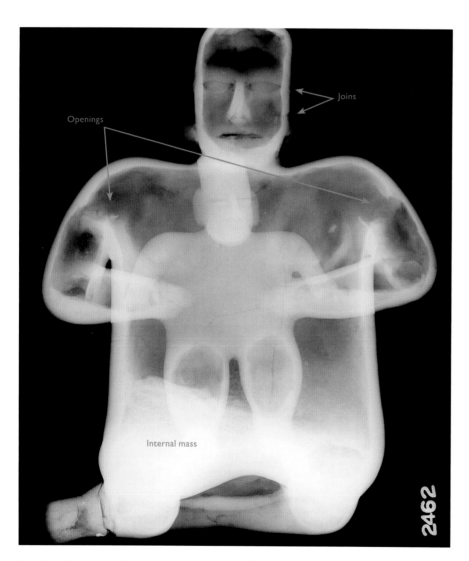

Fig. 1. Overall x-ray showing openings at arms, joins in clay wall, and internal mass. The digital x-ray images here and in figure 2 were captured and viewed using GE Inspection Technologies' digital x-ray equipment and software.

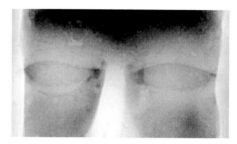

Fig. 2. Detail x-ray image of face, highlighting technique for forming the eyes

Notes

1. Von Winning 1974, figs. 116–214.

2. Viewed on end in the x-radiographs, the clay walls display vertically oriented pores and areas of overlapping clay, both indicative of slab construction. Digital x-ray images were captured and viewed using a GE Inspection Technologies' digital x-ray scanner and software.

3. Other examples of West Mexican ceramics in the collection display this feature; see nos. 35, 51, and checklist no. 34.

4. X-ray fluorescence analysis of the slip detected reduced levels of calcium, iron, and sulfur and enriched levels of aluminum and some titanium. The higher aluminum levels may be linked to a kaolinitic source $(Al_2Si_2O_5(OH)_4)$. The reduced levels of both sulfur and calcium rule out the use of calcium carbonate- or calcium sulfate-based whites.

45. WOMAN WITH VESSEL

Jalisco-Colima, Mexico
300 BCE–100 CE
Burnished earthenware
36.5 × 17.5 × 15.3 cm
TL.2009.20.180

The substantial legs and long, ropelike arms are characteristics of artistic styles of southern Nayarit. Yet the proportions of the head and the open basket carried on the figure's head follow neighboring Jalisco traditions. The woman grasps the rim of a four-footed basket that is secured to her head by a tumpline enlaced around its base. When viewed from the front, however, the lady appears to grab the edge of the vessel, that is, her own body. This is a wonderful dual-reference artwork: we are to understand the piece as a sculptural rendering of a woman carrying an urn-shaped basket on her head whereas her figural position accentuates identity of the object as a vessel.

The woman is depicted nude and devoid of adornment. Such figural simplicity highlights the tiered curvature of the jar—wide at the bottom and gracefully tapering inward as it rises into a classic Meso-american jar form. The woman's ropelike arms serve as an elegant visual directive focusing the eye upward to the vessel's orifice—that is, the basket behind her head. When viewed in profile, the lady's pregnant condition is obvious. The primary message imparted by this vessel-as-vignette is the visual articulation of a woman's revered role as provider and progenitor.

46. FIGURE OF AUTHORITY

Ixtlán del Río, Nayarit, Mexico

300 BCE–200 CE

Earthenware, slip paint

47.6 × 28.8 × 14.6 cm

TL.2009.20.161

The conical hat, short-shafted spear, striped tunic, and multiringed ear and nose ornaments indicate a person of high rank and military affiliation. Whether this figure represents a warrior, a ruler, or other member of the nobility—or a combination thereof—is unknown and perhaps not germane to its semantic intent. Military aptitude was likely an obligatory characteristic of an efficacious leader.

This figure's substantial torso and stocky legs and feet typify the Ixtlán del Río style. They impart a strong monumentality to the sculpture that is independent of the artwork's small size. These features also emphasize the impression of a person of considerable sociopolitical authority.

The Nayarit sculptor used slip paint to render details of clothing decoration that must have been typical of the now-lost textile traditions of ancient West Mexico. Although no textiles survive from the Late Preclassic and Early Classic periods, costuming remains an important part of social identity among indigenous peoples in the region today. The focus on rendering details of costume on the ancient sculptures underscores the longstanding importance of textiles in West Mexico. Here the artist painted vertical stripes and geometric designs on the man's tunic and conical head gear in an effort to depict the elaborately woven cloth worn by this high-status individual.

Technical Commentary

This object has been broken in four places and repaired at the neck, arms, and legs. Portions of the earrings are restorations. The x-ray image (fig. 1) shows that the figure's head, body, and feet are hollow, while the arms and weapon are solid. Both applied clay (the figure's adornments) and incised lines (teeth, toenails, eyes) were employed as surface decoration techniques. There is a single, circular air vent on the back of the hat (fig. 2). The ceramic body is bright red clay, covered with a red/orange iron-based slip.[1] White and yellow painted slip was used to create the pattern of lines and dots on the figure's clothing; the figure's teeth and the pattern on the figure's hat were painted with white slip. The black accretions on the surface contain manganese (JA).[2]

Notes

1. The presence of iron in the red slip was identified through x-ray fluorescence (XRF).

2. "Manganese stains" or manganese oxide accretions (identified here by XRF) are known to form on West Mexican ceramics: O'Grady 2005, 183–92.

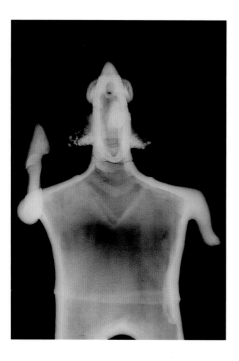

Fig. 1 (left). X-ray image of no. 46. The less dense, short lines in the ceramic body may represent organic inclusions, firing cracks, or the addition of organic temper. The digital x-ray image was captured and viewed using GE Inspection Technologies' digital x-ray equipment and software.

Fig. 2 (right). Back of no. 46

47

47. SEATED MAN

San Sebastián Red, Jalisco, Mexico

300 BCE–200 CE

Earthenware, slip

63.4 × 36 × 22.5 cm

2009.20.32

48. SEATED WOMAN

Nayarit, Mexico

300 BCE–200 CE

Burnished, incised, and slip-painted earthenware

28.9 × 25.5 × 15.5 cm

TL.2009.20.168

These two exceptional explorations of the human form share a number of characteristics that underscore the fact that ancient artistic styles throughout West Mexico do not conform to modern political boundaries despite our use of Mexican states to name the region's ancient cultures. Their similar facial features and figural abstraction attest to connections between the San Sebastián Red style of Jalisco and the Lagunillas pottery sculptures of adjacent Nayarit.[1]

The male figure's serene countenance and seated position on a bench-throne suggest a person of high status, his composed visage intimating that he is above the triviality of daily routine. On the other hand, his formal demeanor—arms held away from the body and hands resting securely on the knees—evokes a ritual pose like those of shamanic practices. The lack of any articulation of dress—other than the earrings, composed of a cluster of rounded forms—and the figure's self-possessed expression point to the interpretation of the work as an idealized portrayal of a shaman in trance.

The female figure's facial serenity matches that of the man, although the focus is not her face but rather her voluptuous body. Small, curved arms and rounded legs with delicate feet create an undulating form of lyrical beauty. Sexual maturity is the implicit narrative of this sculpture, implied by the open position of the legs, the hands framing the figure's pelvic area, the articulation of her genitalia, and the use of negative-resist decoration on her abdomen and thighs to draw attention to her reproductive gift. The ample thighs and voluptuous buttocks emphasize the theme of reproductive health and vitality.

Note

1. Kan 1970, 23.

49, 50. STANDING FEMALE FIGURES

Lagunillas "C" type, Nayarit, Mexico
300 BCE–200 CE
Burnished, slip-painted earthenware
No. 49 (2009.20.59): 39.5 × 18.1 × 9.3
No. 50 (2009.20.62): 38.5 × 18.7 × 10

The Lagunillas style of southern Nayarit comprises five different subgroups of these remarkable human sculptures. The "C" type is distinguished by triangular heads that are broad across the forehead and taper to a delicate, pointed chin. Face and body painting is common, and when present, clothing is rendered as highly decorated fabric.

These two women are particularly fine examples of the "C" type, notable for their exuberant face painting, which combines geometric lines with curvilinear forms. Rather than a symmetrical and rather static design covering the entire face, each side features distinct patterns. Although one is tempted to view the figures as a pair, given the apparent mirroring of their unique face painting, differences in body proportions and renderings of the arms and legs challenge this assessment. Variations include the artist's gentle indentation of the head to represent the central part in the hair on no. 50, which contrasts with the slip-painted hair part on the red-painted figure. Their formalized pose of hands framing the abdomen, accentuated thighs, and erect breasts (resembling those of the seated Nayarit female figure, no. 48) suggest sexual maturity and reproductive fecundity.

Technical Commentary

While not a pair, these two objects are similarly constructed and decorated. They were hand-built; evidence of clay manipulation is evident in the x-ray images as variations in thickness of the clay walls. Both figures have hollow heads, bodies, and legs, while their arms and ears are solid. No. 50 has a small, circular air vent below the proper left ear; no. 49 does not have an air vent. Three painted slip colors—white, red, and black—are used as decoration. On both objects, the white was applied first, then the red slip was applied to large portions of the bodies and to the face, neck, and ears. Lastly, black slip was used to represent hair and patterns on the chest, arms, legs, and face. Burnishing marks are visible on both objects.

No. 49 was broken and repaired at the neck; no. 50 is unbroken. The necklace, rendered in black on no. 50, is now mostly missing, but would have resembled that of no. 49 (JA).

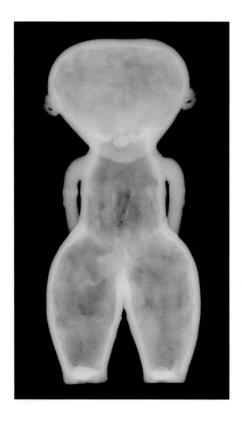 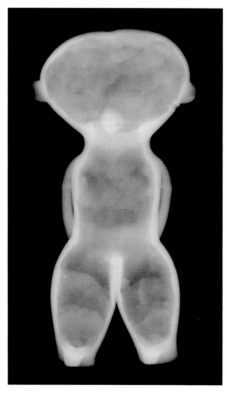

Fig. 1 (left). X-ray image of no. 49. The digital x-ray images here and in figure 2 were captured and viewed using GE Inspection Technologies' digital x-ray equipment and software.

Fig. 2 (right). X-ray image of no. 50

49

50

51. SEATED MALE

Lagunillas "C" type, Nayarit, Mexico
300 BCE–200 CE
Burnished earthenware, slip paint
46.2 × 27.2 × 35.4 cm
2009.20.61

Lagunillas figures often portray men, usually in a seated position with elbows resting on bent knees and forearms crossed on top of each other. The torso leans forward, and the face gazes downward. This figure's loins are wrapped in a relatively wide hip cloth of unadorned fabric. He wears a textile or plant fiber triple-strand band around his head, a forelock of hair falling below the band. His face is extensively painted with black designs, including masklike half circles around his eyes and whiskerlike motifs extending outward from the corners of his mouth. Arm and ankle bands, perhaps made of cut shell, adorn his limbs; similar multistringed ornaments have been found adorning corporeal remains in many tombs from this region.

Technical Commentary

X-radiography reveals that the figure's head, body, and legs are hollow, while the arms, feet, nose, and ears are solid. There is an oval-shaped vent hole in the top of the head. The object appears unbroken, although the highly burnished surface is abraded. Like the other Lagunillas figures, its surface is decorated with white, red, and black slip, applied in that order. White is used for the face and jewelry, red for the body, ears, and headband, and black for the hair, jewelry, and designs on the face and body (JA).

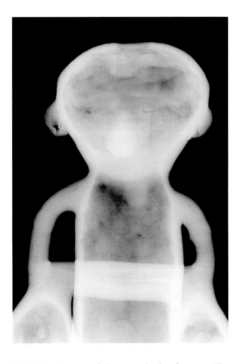

Fig. 1. X-ray image of the upper body of no. 51. The digital x-ray image was captured and viewed using GE Inspection Technologies' digital x-ray equipment and software.

52. GROUP OF FIGURINES AND ARCHITECTURAL MODEL

Colima, Mexico

200 BCE–400 CE

Earthenware

2009.20.33.1 (hut): 16.9 × 13.1 × 13.7 cm

2009.20.33.2–10 (figurines): height 7.1–14.16 cm

Narrative groupings of figurines in architectural settings have been found throughout Mesoamerica in contexts dating as early as the Middle Formative Period (900–400 BCE). Some are made from jadeite and similar precious stones, such as an Olmec ceremonial scene of sixteen figurines arranged in a semicircle and framed by six columnlike celts.[1] Others are composed of modeled ceramic figures depicting a burial or ancestor veneration rite complete with elaborately dressed performers and musicians, like that found above Tomb 103 at Monte Albán, Oaxaca.[2] The objects that constitute these figure groups generally share the same aesthetic style and manufacturing technique, which suggests they were made at the same time as a single artistic statement.

The disparate artistic styles and technical features suggest that these nine Colima figurines and one building model might be a modern grouping, although dissimilar figurines have been documented in figure groupings found in the same tomb. In this instance archaeological confirmation is not available.[3] The figurine types represent at least two styles from Colima-Jalisco, including the Tuxcacuesco-Ortices type (nos. 33.3, 33.8, and 33.9) and two from the Colima-Jalisco border region (nos. 33.4 and 33.5). The house model (no. 33.1) depicts a typical West Mexican domicile or ceremonial building without its basal, earthen platform. No architecture of comparable form is found in the region because these structures were made of perishable materials; only the earth-and-stone platforms have survived, although many have been destroyed by modern agricultural activities. These architectural models thus document the lost architectural heritage of ancient West Mexico.[4]

The figures portray men and women performing both ritual and daily activities, from mothers tending children (nos. 33.3 and 33.8) and grinding maize (no. 33.7) to men drumming (no. 33.6) or sitting regally and brandishing a fanlike scepter (no. 33.9). A seated hunchback figure, which also is a whistle, sports an elaborate head wrap and fine jewelry (no. 33.10). A dog-standing-atop-a-dog sculpture and two seated men with elongated heads complete the group (nos. 33.2, 33.4, and 33.5). This elongated-head figurine style is associated with the northern Colima-Jalisco region and dates to the later years of the Comala phase (ca. 200–300 CE).

Notes

1. San Francisco 2010, 160–61, pl. 72

2. New York 1970, 200–201, no. 163.

3. Los Angeles 1970, 147, nos. 143a–o. See also New York 1970, no. 98.

4. Los Angeles 1972. See also Townsend 1998b.

53, 54. TEMPLE MODELS

Mezcala style, Central Río Balsas area,
Guerrero, Mexico
Terminal Formative to Early Classic Periods,
300 BCE–500 CE (?)
Stone
No. 53 (TL.2009.20.160): 16 × 7.5 × 2.5 cm
No. 54 (2009.20.4): 19.4 × 15.5 × 2 cm

The Mezcala sculptural style of Guerrero emphasizes geometric abstraction in both human figures and architectural models. Few examples have been found in their original context, and thus the function, meaning, and even the length of time during which the style was in use remain ill defined. Contributing to the question of chronology is the fact that other Mesoamerican peoples, from the latter centuries of the Late Formative to the Late Postclassic periods (200–1500 CE), acquired and preserved these works as heirlooms.

They have been found at sites throughout Mexico, and large numbers were excavated from ritual caches in the Templo Mayor, the main temple of the fifteenth-century Mexica (Aztecs) of Tenochtitlan (Mexico City).[1] In the twentieth century, the minimalistic Mezcala artworks fascinated the Mexican artist and cultural historian Miguel Covarrubias, who compared them favorably to other sculptural traditions such as the celebrated Cycladic style of ancient Greece.

These two examples feature the typical Mezcala four-columned structure atop a pyramidal platform articulated by apron-moldings on the uppermost tier. A central staircase leads into the structure at the midpoint between the columns. On no. 53 two figures stand atop its gently sloping roof; a lone figure stands between the columns and inside the structure on the other example (no. 54). No buildings of this type have

survived in Guerrero, however, which leaves open the question of whether these carvings faithfully represent the architectural traditions of the region during the Formative and Classic periods. The authenticity of both pieces is under study.

Note

1. Matos Moctezuma 1984, 149.

53

54

55. DOG EFFIGY VESSEL

Jalisco, Mexico

300 BCE–200 CE

Burnished earthenware

20.8 × 35.4 × 19 cm

2009.20.23

56. DOG EFFIGY VESSEL

Comala, Colima, Mexico

100 BCE–300 CE

Burnished earthenware

25 × 36.3 × 21.9 cm

TL.2009.20.178

57. DOG EFFIGY VESSEL

Colima, Mexico

300 BCE–200 CE

Burnished earthenware

18.2 × 26.4 × 12.3 cm

TL.2009.20.176

Dogs were indigenous to the ancient Americas, the Mexican Hairless being the likely model for the West Mexico effigies. Throughout Mesoamerica they served as companions, hunting partners, underworld guides, and even sources of food. Ceramic portrayals of dogs are particularly numerous in the shaft tombs of West Mexico, placed among the burials' myriad human pottery figures and dishes of food for the journey after death.

Most dogs are depicted as plump and docile, like the two Colima examples here. One (no. 57) is modeled in a more abstract form, whereas the dark red canine (no. 56) more realistically illustrates the breed's physical characteristics. As tomb offerings, these fattened versions may have symbolized food for the deceased's arduous underworld voyage. The black-slipped canine (no. 55) deftly combines a jar form, the most important vessel in the Mesoamerican household, with an appealing rendering of a smiling dog. In this example, the dog's ribs recall the flutes of a gourd, the ageless and most common food-service vessel throughout the ancient Americas. Considered as a whole, this vessel-sculpture's multiple references to food suggest that it too alludes to dogs as sustenance.

55

56

57

58

58. DOG EFFIGY

Comala, Colima, Mexico
100 BCE–300 CE
Earthenware, red slip with black paint
34.6 × 48.6 × 29.3 cm
2009.20.51

59. DOG EFFIGY VESSEL

Comala, Colima, Mexico
100 BCE–300 CE
Earthenware, burnished slip paint in
red and light brown
14.3 × 30.9 × 27.8 cm
2009.20.63

60. HOWLING DOG EFFIGY

Jalisco, Mexico
300 BCE–200 CE
Earthenware, slip paint
24 × 32.1 × 14.8 cm
TL.2009.20.148

Among the Mexica (Aztecs) of highland Mexico, dogs were associated with the deity Xolotl, the god of death. This deity and a dog were believed to lead the soul on its journey to the underworld.[1] The Mexica also associated Xolotl with the planet Venus as the evening star (portrayed with the head of a canine) and the twin brother of the deity Quetzalcóatl, who personified Venus as the morning star.

The dog's special relationship with humans is highlighted by a number of Colima dog effigies wearing humanoid masks. This curious effigy type has been interpreted as a shamanic transformation image or as a reference to the modern Huichol myth of the origin of the first wife, who was transformed from a dog into a human.[2] However, recent scholarship suggests a new explanation of these sculptures as the depiction of the animal's *tonalli*, its inner essence, which is made manifest by being given human form via the mask.[3] The use of the human face to make reference to an object's or animal's inner spirit is found in the artworks of many ancient cultures of the Americas, from the Inuit of Alaska and northern Canada to peoples in Argentina and Chile.[4]

These extraordinary depictions of dogs—one attentive (no. 58), another reclining (no. 59), and a third howling (no. 60)—capture their spirit as companions of humans. The attentive canine's rotund body may suggest its value as food for the posthumous soul. The reclining dog has seemingly just woken, slightly raising its head and perking up its ears in reaction to whatever disturbed its slumber. The artist skillfully modeled its body, especially the muscles and skeletal features. The white-slipped dog's elongated body and animated legs capture the effort of a boisterous howl or bark. The slightly raised rear legs suggest that the animal is ready to run after the offending entity that prompted his enmity. The white hue and skinny body might also have underworld connotations, although such an interpretation is not certain in this instance.

Notes

1. Toscano 1946, 9–33.
2. Furst 1998, 186.
3. Ibid., 185–87, fig. 26.
4. Ibid., 186–87, fig. 28.

61. FEMALE FIGURE

Chupícuaro, Guanajuato
300 BCE–100 CE
Earthenware, slip paint in red,
white, and black
25.3 × 10.2 × 5.4 cm
TL.2009.20.236

62. FOOTED DISH

Chupícuaro, Guanajuato
300 BCE–100 CE
Earthenware, slip paint in red,
white, and black
Height 13.2 cm, diameter 23.9 cm
TL.2009.20.169

The distinctive Chupícuaro style was first identified at the urban center of the same name located in southern Guanajuato. The site was covered by a reservoir in 1948 to supply water for Mexico City. During salvage and later excavations in the region, pottery vessels and figures in the Chupícuaro style were found at sites along the Lerma River and southward in the vicinity of Lake Cuitzeo in Michoacán. The Chupícuaro region had longstanding cultural and trade connections with the Valley of Mexico beginning as early as 200 BCE, indicated by similarities in ceramic figural art traditions from both regions. In addition, artistic similarities are found in objects from Jalisco, Nayarit, and Colima, strongly intimating a strategic role for Chupícuaro as a point-of-transfer and unifying power linking Central and West Mexican peoples for many centuries.[1]

Burials of members of the Chupícuaro elite typically included a large number of female figures that conceptually link death with fertility as a central precept of the Mesoamerican ideology of death, transformation, and regeneration.[2] Larger sculptures are hollow, but the majority are solid, modeled figures. Typically, the figures' basic features are defined by modeling; the ornately woven clothing and the striking body painting, a hallmark of Chupícuaro figures, are depicted in paint. On this example (no. 61), the stepped design creates larger diamond-shaped and x-patterned motifs across the woman's body. It is likely these patterns carry symbolic significance. The figure's short pants (or possibly body painting) feature a combined vertical and horizontal patterning that suggests a highly developed weaving tradition, which sadly has not survived. A curious gray-black square is painted at the base of the figure's head, a rare motif eluding interpretation. This same blank field is replicated on the footed dish (no. 62),

although here the blank square is cream in hue. Whether this blank square represents a Chupícuaro aesthetic element or a symbolic form remains unknown.

Notes

1. Jímenez Moreno 1972, 31–36.
2. Townsend 1998b, 116–17.

Chupícuaro towns were no mere village hamlets. Many were populous centers, highly organized and maintained by a hierarchy of administrators and operatives. The society is renowned for an exceptionally sophisticated ceramic tradition featuring large quantities of startling human (mostly female) figural effigies and everyday food-service vessels of notable aesthetic appeal. The wide variety of vessel forms and their decoration point to the importance of the feast, not only to supply food for the soul's journey to the underworld but also among the living as an integral part of social politics. Throughout ancient Mesoamerica, feasts provided an effective stage for a wide variety of sociopolitical activities focused on solidifying relations, forming alliances, and affirming expectations of reciprocity in all matters of support.[1]

Chupícuaro ceramics elevate objects intended for daily use into highly sophisticated artistic achievements, as exemplified by this bowl's elegant form and boldly painted decoration. Its rounded shape and lack of neck, a vessel form called a *tecomate*, recalls the gourd, the quintessential food-service vessel throughout the ancient Americas and among most indigenous societies the world over. The Chupícuaro artist personified the vessel by adorning it with a modeled humanoid visage that simultaneously emerges from and recedes into the *tecomate*'s walls. The integration of an animated human face with a common vessel form infuses the container with life force, the face symbolizing essence and soul power.

Note

1. Reents-Budet 2000, 1022–38. See also Monaghan 1990; Byland and Pohl 1994.

63. BOWL

Chupícuaro, Guanajuato
300 BCE–100 CE
Earthenware, slip paint in red,
white, and black
13.2 × 28 × 30 cm
TL.2009.20.209

64. DANCING FIGURE WHISTLE

Colima, Mexico

300 BCE–200 CE

Earthenware

23.3 × 16.8 × 10.2 cm

2009.20.29

Dance, among the most ephemeral of the arts, was central to Mesoamerican civilization. Dance performances, as attested by their depiction on vases and other utilitarian objects such as this whistle, typically encompassed rhythmic, structured movement, often by a group of people. Music was a vital element, frequently supplied by the dancers themselves.[1] Performances served to bring together the community by reifying shared beliefs of social behavior, recounting seminal histories—both historical and mythic—and incarnating religious ideologies. As communal theater, performers were bedecked in ostentatious costumes that served to remove them from their social identities and the everyday reality of the community. The elaborate costuming and staging also elevated the event from a simple entertainment to an impressive, even iconic spectacle.

This festooned dancer bends his knees and stretches out his arms as if frozen in mid-motion. Small holes in his hands likely accommodated dance fans or other performance accouterments. Necklaces composed of round beads, perhaps of precious jadeite, and a variety of bands adorn his wrists and legs. A wide neckpiece draped over the figure's shoulders and chest may have been made from pieces of cut shell. His sleeveless shirt might represent a tufted textile or animal hide, although it also recalls portrayals of the flayed skin of a sacrificial victim worn by celebrants as part of the rites of the deity Xipe Totec.[2] The dancer's loincloth and overskirt are tied at the back with a large bow that resembles a bustle. A decorated textile band is wrapped adroitly around his head and secured by a strap below his chin. This object is a whistle, likely played by a performer similar to the dancer depicted by the instrument; its mouthpiece is found at the back of the figure's head.

Notes

1. For examples, see Los Angeles 1970, nos. 136 and 143.

2. M. Miller and Taube 1993, 188–89. See also Indianapolis 1988, 158, no. 107.

65. FEMALE RITUAL PERFORMER

Nopiloa, southern Veracruz, Mexico

Late Classic Period, 600–900 CE

Earthenware

40.3 × 24.1 × 10.2 cm

2009.20.47

South-central Veracruz was home to a number of vibrant sculptural traditions. Among them is the so-called Nopiloa style, named for the archaeological site of Nopiloa located in the Mixtequilla area of southern Veracruz.[1] Hundreds, if not thousands, of these striking figures were produced during the Late Classic Period, ranging from small figures to large-scale sculptures, most of which were made in press molds with some hand-modeling for adding accouterments of dress.

The figures may depict ritual performers or intended sacrificial victims in the midst of a trance induced by the ingestion of mind-altering substances such as hallucinogenic plants, animal poisons, or alcohol.[2] It has been suggested that these figures represent the Classic Period antecedents of the ritual practices of induced joviality and ecstatic dance in honor of the Postclassic deity Xochipilli-Macuilzochitl.[3] These Nopiloa figures typically are portrayed with upraised head and arms held at the side of the head. Usually the right hand clutches an object that eludes identification although it has been variously suggested to be a rattle, a potent native tobacco cigar, or a hallucinogenic plant material.

Notes

1. McBride 1971.

2. Heyden 1971.

3. Medellín Zenil and Peterson 1954. See also Nicholson, 1971, 16.

66. DEER HEAD MASK

Remojades or Nopiloa, Veracruz, Mexico

Late Classic Period, 600–900 CE

Earthenware, post-fire paint

10.2 × 10.2 × 10.4 cm

2009.20.2

67. INCENSE BURNER

Colima, Mexico

Early Postclassic Period, 900–1200 CE

Earthenware, post-fire paint

40.3 × 16.3 × 18.2 cm

TL.2009.20.217

Fanciful headdresses were an essential component of performance costumes because they were crucial to the dancers' perceived transformation into the personage or spirit being in whose guise they performed. In Veracruz, figurines depicting warriors and a wide variety of performers often wear full-head masks, which can be removed to reveal the person inside, such as the amazingly detailed head-mask of a deer (no. 66).[1] Post-fire paint adorns the animal, with black-line curvilinear motifs on his long ear and bright blue-green pigment embellishing his upper lip. Large protuberances on his snout and the single horn atop his head suggest a composite zoomorph rather than a biologically accurate rendering. The deer was an important Mesoamerican food source, and its hide was used for a variety of purposes including the wrapping of ritual bundles and as leaves (pages) for screen-fold manuscripts which contained all manner of knowledge—from history to religious mythology to astrology and astronomy. The deer also was the animal spirit form of the mother of the seminal Mexican deity Quetzalcóatl and of the wife of the maize god among the Classic Maya.[2]

The innovative incense burner of Postclassic Colima (no. 67) is composed of back-to-back figures, their heads merging to form the container for burning coals and incense. The handle also serves as the figures' imaginative headdresses, its tall arch providing support for an undulating serpent attached at the front. Similar saurian forms are found today on the headdresses and masks of ritual performers in Colima and Guerrero. The conjoined figures' outstretched arms and wide stance are strikingly similar to those of the Veracruz ritual dancers (see no. 65), which prompts a similar identification for this unusual type of anthropomorphic incense burner.

Notes

1. Goldstein 1988, 69–71, nos. 105–12.

2. M. Miller and Taube 1993, 74–75.

68. MUSICIAN-SINGER

Zacatecas, Jalisco-Zacatecas
border region, Mexico
100–300 CE
Earthenware, slip paint
39.1 × 22.9 × 18.9 cm
TL.2009.20.194

69. SLIT DRUM

Maya, Campeche, Mexico
Late Postclassic period, 1350–1521 CE
Wood, possibly sapote
Drum: 26.5 × 8.8 × 30.4 cm;
drumstick a: length 54.4 cm, diameter 4.5 cm;
drumstick b: length 53.8 cm, diameter 5 cm
TL.2009.20.193

68

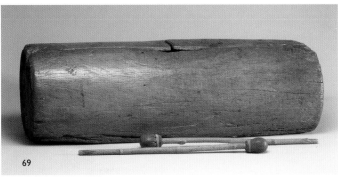

69

The distinctive Zacatecas-style figurine tradition was created in a relatively small region along the Jalisco-Zacatecas border. Figures in the style primarily represent seated males, especially persons of authority and drummers-singers, as in this example. Seated women with hands resting on the abdomen also are known, likely related to the theme of sexual maturity found among other ancient art styles throughout West Mexico.

This sculpture is a fine example of Zacatecas-style figurines, notable for their expert modeling and painted decoration. Here a performer plays a single-headed drum held between his knees and sings or chants in accompaniment (note his open mouth and pursed lips). The rich overlay of colors and dramatic design elements reveals the artist's mastery of the challenging medium of slip paint. The man's face is highlighted by the use of a cream-hued slip and dynamic black lines representing face painting. His ankles and feet are differentiated by the lack of any decoration. The figure's protruding, red-painted ears, pierced for earrings, accentuate his oval eyes and the enigmatic "horns" atop his head. Such hornlike appendages are characteristic of the Zacatecas figural style; their significance remains a matter of speculation but may distinguish shamanic practitioners.[1]

Drums were among the most important of instruments played during ritual performances, warfare, and state pageants such as formal visits and rites of enthronement. Drums directed warriors on the battlefield, announced the beginning of ceremonial events, and provided rhythm for processions and dances. Drums of many varieties are pictured in Mesoamerican art, and a few have survived such as this large, wooden slit-drum (or *tunkul*, in Yucatec Mayan). Other artworks and ethnohistoric information indicate that the larger drums often were played by more than one musician.[2]

Notes

1. Meighan and Nicholson 1970, 62–63
2. For example, see Los Angeles 1972, 25, nos. 125–28, 130.

70

71

72

73

70, 71. BALLGAME PERFORMERS

Colima-Jalisco, Mexico
100 BCE–300 CE
Earthenware, slip paint in red, black, and white
No. 70 (TL.2009.20.133): 19.6 × 8 × 3.2 cm
No. 71 (TL.2009.20.134): 19 × 8.5 × 2.8 cm

72, 73. BALLGAME (?) PERFORMERS

Tuxcacuesco-Ortices, Jalisco-Colima, Mexico
300 BCE–200 CE
Earthenware, traces of black paint
No. 72 (TL.2009.20.172): 17.8 × 10.9 × 2.8 cm
No. 73 (TL.2009.20.175): 18.1 × 10.2 × 3.8 cm

The Mesoamerican ballgame was part of a ceremonial complex that included dance, music, and drama, and often was associated with warfare and solemn rites of cosmic renewal. Its ceremonial components—from parades to ritual dance performances to sacrificial rites—constituted a potent collective activity that reinforced social cohesion.[1] Given the importance of these ceremonies, it is not surprising that Mesoamerican art is filled with portrayals of ballplayers as performers.

These two styles of figurines from the Jalisco-Colima area of West Mexico portray ballplayers bedecked in the wide belts and arm bands (arm protectors) typical of ballgame gear. Their pose communicates readiness for the intense action of the game, while their large ear and nose ornaments, ample necklaces, and multiple textile head bands suggest the kind of ornate attire frequently worn by performers. Whether the two Tuxcacuesco-Ortices style figurines depict ballplayers is uncertain, although their wide belts are characteristic of such portrayals. One (no. 71) may represent a female, suggested by the slightly enlarged breasts, although gender is often ambiguous in Tuxcacuesco-Ortices figurines.[2] The figure's loin covering resembles the male loincloth but also recalls the bound-grass covering worn by females. This figurine is further notable for the hornlike protuberance on the forehead, although it remains uncertain whether it represents a shaman's horn, an emblem of power, or some other headdress element.[3]

Notes

1. Day 1998, 167.

2. Kelly 1949, 115.

3. Furst 1998, 188, figs. 29, 30.

74. RITUAL DANCER OCARINA (VESSEL FLUTE)

Remojades, south-central Veracruz

600–800 CE

Earthenware

28.2 × 17.6 × 7 cm

TL.2009.20.211

Sound has always been a crucial component of public events—whether solemn religious ceremonies, persuasive political activities, or celebratory enjoyment. Sound highlights and gives sensory shape to the event.[1] Throughout the ancient Americas, sound was considered an intermediary between ritual events on earth and the gods in whose honor many rites were held. Thus Mesoamerican peoples created a variety of wind instruments (aerophones), such as whistles, flutes and ocarinas, rasps and rattles (idiophones), and drums (membranophones) made of animal skins stretched over wood or ceramic forms. The music of modern indigenous American cultures echoes its ancient forms, although much has been lost. These instruments, which carried a variety of allegorical meanings and associations, emphasize the social importance and highly developed aesthetics of these now-silent musical scores.

This effigy is more than a figure—it also is an ocarina, the vessel flute's mouthpiece pierced at the top center of the head.[2] Combining a mold-made head and appliquéd accouterments of dress and adornment, the figural portrayal is typical of the Remojades style of so-called Remojades Smiling Figures, named for the archaeological site of Remojades that sits at the northern edge of the Jamapa River system just south of the modern port city of Veracruz. Remojades-style figures typically wear a loincloth with long tie-ends and a single or multiple bands around the upper chest. This figure's characteristic pendant is particularly large, the central diadem likely representing a cut *Oliva* shell fashioned into a bell. His hair is indicated by a simple portrayal of a short haircut, although the central, raised band suggests the alternative identification of close-fitting head gear. The figure's outstretched arms and hands, with thumbs pointing downward, and the wide stance aptly convey the movement of a dancer.

Notes

1. Sullivan 1986, 15.

2. Olsen 2002, 100–126.

75. SEATED NOBLEMAN OCARINA (VESSEL FLUTE)

Jaina, Campeche, Mexico

Late Classic Period, 550–850 CE

Earthenware, post-fire paint

16.3 × 6.9 × 7.8 cm

TL.2009.20.259

Vessel flutes, called ocarinas in the Americas, frequently are used by shamanic practitioners today as a vehicle of call or communication with the spirit world.[1] The same purpose likely extends back in time to the earliest human societies in the hemisphere. This ocarina's mouthpiece and air duct are found on the figure's right shoulder and back. When played, the seated figure would face roughly forward.

This wind instrument renders a seated man with arms crossed over his chest in a formal pose. His fine attire and regal bearing imply nobility, the ocarina/figurine perhaps portraying a ruler given the iconic meanings of the motifs on his face, produced either by intentional scarification or face-painting. His right cheek displays the "jester god," an emblem of royalty which aligned the wearer with the maize god and the power of agricultural fertility and world renewal.[2] Such affiliation is further connoted by the sprouting maize plant depicted in the center of his brow which recalls the trefoil crown of the maize god and of Maya kings. This royal crown, replete with its sprouting maize icon, has its origins among the Olmecs of the Formative Period (1200–500 BCE).[3] This regal Maya ocarina/figurine also sports a long loincloth and hip wrap, and his body is adorned with impressively large earflares and a shell pendant.

Notes

1. Olsen 2002, 100.

2. Fields 1991, 167–74. See also Fort Worth 1986, 53.

3. Los Angeles 2005, 26, nos. 13–17.

76. TURKEY EFFIGY OCARINA

Colima, Mexico

300 BCE–200 CE

Earthenware

12.5 × 13.4 × 7.6 cm

TL.2009.20.95

77. MAN-BIRD EFFIGY OCARINA

Veracruz, Mexico

Late Classic Period, 600–900 CE

Earthenware, black paint

20.2 × 17.6 × 14.3 cm

TL.2009.20.139

Sixteenth-century Spanish chroniclers recount the playing of ocarinas by Aztec participants and audience members alike during processions in Tenochtitlan (Mexico City). The simplicity of playing an ocarina removed the instrument from one of exclusivity requiring extensive practice in order to create an acceptable musical score. The ocarina was widely used among the peoples of Mesoamerica, and examples have been found by archaeologists in both palaces and the humble abodes of commoners.

These two ocarinas are of the type found in prodigious numbers among all societies of ancient Mesoamerica and elsewhere in the Americas. Mesoamerican artworks, from carved stone panels to painted books, often render warriors, dancers, and other performers playing this type of instrument.[1] The Colima ocarina (no. 76) portrays an anthropomorphic turkey with a little dog perched atop its opened tail feathers. The Veracruz instrument (no. 77) represents a person wearing an impressively large eagle or other raptorial bird headdress, secured by a wide strap underneath his chin. It may portray a member of a warrior order similar to the famed Eagle Warrior order of the Aztecs. The two tiny holes pierced through the center of the ocarina allowed it to be attached to a cord and worn around the neck during battle or processions.

Note

1. See, for example, von Winning 1974, 104, no. 38

78. CONCH SHELL TRUMPET EFFIGY

Colima, Mexico
300 BCE–200 CE
Earthenware, white slip or ground
13.2 × 24.2 × 16.3 cm
TL.2009.20.111

Throughout the ancient Americas, conch shell trumpets punctuated significant earthly events, including the arrival of dignitaries at state functions, on the battlefield as a signal to engage the enemy or otherwise direct the regiments, and during religious rites to accentuate the peak spiritual moment. The conch shell also had long-standing symbolic associations with the watery underworld and was connected to certain deities. At Teotihuacan, images of conch shells adorned buildings whose decorative narratives indicate their relationship to agricultural plenty and the gods' place of Creation. At Teotihuacan and among various peoples of West Mexico, conch shells denoted high status and special spiritual power, frequently being found in burials of the elite and adorning figures to denote a shaman's supernatural powers.[1] The Aztec deity Quetzalcóatl, the god of wind, wore a cross-sectioned conch shell as his special emblem, and members of the Mexica elite also wore the wind jewel as a proclamation of authority.

Conch shell trumpets were fashioned from the natural shell or replicated in ceramic, as is this example. Shell trumpets are especially plentiful in the shaft tombs of West Mexico where they were intimately associated with elite status and shamanic power. They often are illustrated being played by persons depicted in the anecdotal sculptures for which the region is famous, these sculptural narratives illustrating ballgames, funerary processions, accession rites, and many other communal events of social and religious import.[2]

Notes

1. Von Winning 1974, 17.

2. Los Angeles 1972.

79. ZOOMORPHIC EFFIGY TUBULAR DUCT FLUTE

Veracruz, Mexico
Late Classic Period, 600–900 CE
Earthenware
29.5 × 18.9 × 4 cm
TL.2009.20.137

Extensively decorated with modeled imagery, duct flutes of Veracruz comprise a *tour-de-force* of aesthetics and musical functional form deftly merged into a singular visual and auditory creation. The tubular duct flute of Veracruz is characterized by one or two connected sounding tubes. Along its shaft(s) or at its end are found two semi-circular disks or a full disk at whose center is a modeled ritual performer or a zoomorph of likely symbolic identity, as is the case with the peccary head at the center of this flute's disk. No myths have survived from ancient Veracruz that feature the peccary, although among the contemporary Maya of southern Mesoamerica the peccary was related to the pillars of the cosmos, and various nobles included its name in their elite nominal phrases. Among the Huichol of northwestern Mexico, the peccary is associated with the earth god.

These Veracruz flutes are notable for having clay pellets inside their tubular chambers. The small clay balls produce an eerie, warbling sound when the flute is played, although it takes skill to elicit the full range of auditory features made possible by this structural innovation. The high-quality craftsmanship and detailed, symbolic decoration of this flute imply its social and ritual importance as a special instrument intended for use during rites of significance rather than more commonplace public ceremonies.

80. ANTHROPOMORPHIC TUBULAR DUCT FLUTE

Veracruz or Maya, southern Veracruz or
Tabasco, Mexico
Late Classic Period, 600–900 CE
Earthenware, traces of post-fire paint
20.7 × 8.1 × 6.3 cm
TL.2009.20.135

81. DOUBLE-CHAMBERED TUBULAR DUCT FLUTE

Colima, Mexico
300 BCE–200 CE
Earthenware
23.2 × 6.5 × 5.4 cm
TL.2009.20.102

82. ANTHROPOMORPHIC TUBULAR DUCT FLUTE

Colima, Mexico
300 BCE–200 CE
Earthenware, partially burnished,
traces of post-fire paint (blue, white)
26.5 × 7.7 × 6.2 cm
TL.2009.20.138

These three tubular duct flutes illustrate the variety of aerophones that typify the musical instrument repertoire of different societies during Late Classic times in Mesoamerica. They share the modeling of the human figure as their primary decorative program, but these range from the dramatic naturalism of near portraiture seen on the Veracruz or Maya flute (no. 80), to the schematized portrayal on the fluted instrument, and ending with the extreme minimalism of the figural rendering on the double-chambered flute from Colima (no. 81). Each instrument holds its unique potential for creating a variety of tones and sounds of different timbres, depending on the force of wind entering the mouthpiece and sound chamber(s) as well as the positioning of the player's fingers (when applicable). Although the casual musician can produce acceptable sounds from these instruments, practiced skill is required to achieve their full effect.

83. MINIATURE STELA

Maya, Uaymil, Campeche, Mexico
810 CE
Limestone
56.5 × 12.8 × 9.7 cm
TL.2009.20.196

This miniature stela reportedly came from Uaymil, a site of modest size on a small island off the north coast of Campeche. In spite of its relatively small size, Uaymil played an important role as a transshipment zone during the Late Classic and Early Post-classic periods (650–1300 CE), facilitating the movement of goods throughout southern Mesoamerica. Miniature stelae are rare and are found exclusively in Campeche and Yucatan. They likely were placed on altars or benches inside administrative or ancestral shrine buildings.

All four sides of this tiny monument are carved. The front features an elaborately attired lord, likely a ruler, presiding over a period-ending ceremony. He sports a long cape and casts incense from the bag clutched in his left hand onto a small altar at his feet. His zoomorphic headdress is topped by a bird with outstretched wings, the headdress's two hieroglyphs likely having recorded the nobleman's name (now eroded). A deified ancestor floats above his descendant, providing supernatural power and legitimacy to the ruler's acts. The other three sides of the monument carry a detailed hieroglyphic text beginning on the left side. The text eludes full decipherment because of surface erosion and the occasional unusual hieroglyph or phrase.

The text opens on the left side with an overly large ISIG (Initial Series Introductory Glyph). As is typical of Yucatecan monuments, the ISIG is followed by the Short Count notation (A1–A3), omitting the Long Count that is seen on most Classic Maya monuments. The Short Count date is *13*

Ajaw 3 Ihk'sihoom (*13 Ahau 3 Ch'en* in the conventional Yucatec terminology), and it is followed by a *19 tun* designation (at A4). The only calendrical placement that accords with all of these calendrical notations is *9.18.19.0.0 13 Ahau 3 Ch'en*, or July 3, 809 CE. Unfortunately, the rest of the passage is eroded, although readable at A5–A6 is *sakjal baak uk'in* "blanching bone, its day" (free translation:, "blanching bone is the day of . . . after . . .").[1] This rare phrase may signify some kind of quality or attribute of the date.

The text continues on the back with the new Long Count date *9.19.0.0.0 9 Ahau* [18 Mol], or June 28, 810 CE, which falls precisely 360 days (*1 tun*) after the date on the stela's left side. The rear text, too, is highly eroded and little syntax can be reconstructed. However, visible at B9–C9 is a restatement of the date *9 Ahau*, which is qualified as a *k'altuun* or "stone-binding," a ritual event involving the wrapping of the stela in cloth.[2] It is likely that the lord's name follows at B10–C10, after which the text is completely illegible.

Most of the right side text remains opaque, although the paired 16-?[K'IN] 9-?[K'IN] formula (at D3 and D5) recalls the names or titles of period-ending deities in the inscriptions at Palenque and elsewhere.[3] The *9 Ahau* phrase is repeated at D6, followed by what may be a dedicatory phrase for the monument (D9-?). If correct, this phrase would imply a carving date of 810 CE, which would suggest its having been made to commemorate the 9.19.0.0.0 period ending June 28, 810 CE (MZ / DR-B).

Notes

1. Houston et al. 2009, 21–22.

2. Stuart 1996.

3. See Guenter 2007 for discussion.

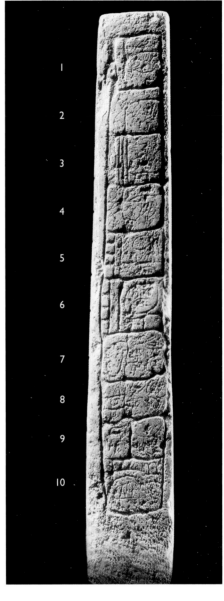

Left Side Text

A1 (ISIG, eroded Haab patron)

A2 13-AJAW

A3 3-[IHK']SIHOOM-TE'

A4 19-TUUN-ni

A5 SAK-ja-la-BAAK

A6 u-K'IN-ni

A7 ?-?-li

A8 PAAT?-?

Back Side Text

B1–C1 (ISIG, eroded Haab patron)

B2 9-PIK	C2 19-WINIKHAAB
B3 0-HAAB	C3 0-WINAL
B4 0-K'IN	C4 9-AJAW
B5 17/18?-?	C5 18-?
B6 9?-?	C6 ?-?
B7 ?	C7 chi?-?
B8 ?	C8 EK'?
B9 9-AJAW	C9 K'AL?[TUUN-ni]
B10 ?-IXIM?	C10 CHAN-TOK'?-?
B11 9?-?-?-PET?	C11 ?-?
B12 CH'AM?	C12 ma-AK'AB?

Right Side Text

D1 6-yo?-?

D2 u-TAL?

D3 16-?[K'IN]-ni

D4 u-TAL?

D5 9-?[K'IN]-ni

D6 9-AJAW

D7 i?-T'AB?

D8 ?-?

D9 ?-TUUN?-ni

D10 ?-?

84. WARRIOR FIGURINE

Maya, Jaina Island area, Campeche, Mexico

Late Classic Period, 550–850 CE

Earthenware, post-fire paint

22.7 × 10.2 × 6.2 cm

2009.20.38

Among the most renowned of the myriad figurine traditions of Mesoamerica is that of Jaina Island, a residential and funerary settlement adjacent to the coast of west-central Campeche. Jaina Island's extensive burial grounds have been known since the nineteenth century, but only in the 1940s were they first scientifically excavated.[1] Archaeologists found figurines in the arms of the deceased who had been dressed in their finest clothes and wrapped in cotton burial shrouds and palm-fiber mats. The renowned Mexico archaeologist Román Piña Chan, the director of excavations at Jaina, has speculated that the figurines served to ensure the deceased's lifeways and social position in the afterlife.[2]

This figurine is notable because it portrays an elderly warrior rather than the robust young combatant so typical of Classic Maya figurines. His identity is confirmed by the flexible, rectangular shield held in his right hand and the quilted armor tunic, both being requisite garb for Maya warriors. He likely represents a captured warrior, defiant yet stately in demeanor, his defeat indicated by the thick rope binding his neck and upper arms. The form of the head suggests that the figure originally was adorned with a removable headdress which has been lost.

Technical Commentary

The torso and upper legs of this earthenware figure are hollow, while the arms and lower legs are solid. The x-ray image (fig. 1) shows that the hollow, upper portions of the legs were finished, and the solid lower portions of the legs were subsequently attached. There are three small, circular vent holes—one on the front, center of the figure's torso, and two on the back—one on each side of the figure's lower back. Both applied clay (ruffle collar, shield) and mold-made elements (torso with patterned tunic) are utilized for surface decoration. Elevated levels of magnesium were detected in the blue pigment present on the figure's hips.[3] The lack of other elements associated with blue colorants suggests the presence of the magnesium-containing clay, attapulgite, used by the Maya to create the pigment Maya Blue which has been identified on other Jaina figurines.[4] The figure is broken and repaired. Repair and restoration material at the neck and both legs are evident. The proper right foot is a restoration (JA).

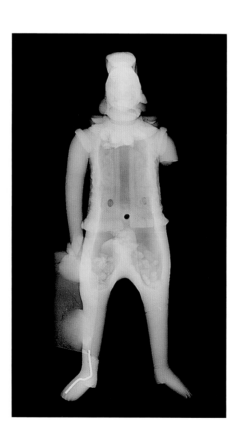

Fig. 1. X-radiograph of no. 84. Breaks and repairs in the legs and at the neck are evident. The figure is hollow and contains loose, pebblelike material, visible in the upper legs.

Notes

1. Piña Chan 1968.

2. Schele 1997, 16.

3. X-ray fluorescence was used to identify the composition of the blue pigment.

4. Maya Blue is a mixture of attapulgite clay and indigo. José-Yacaman et al. 1996, 223–25; Leona et al. 2004.

85. MASKED MALE FIGURE

Maya, Jaina Island area, Campeche, Mexico
Late Classic Period, 700–900 CE
Earthenware, post-fire paint
18.4 × 11.4 × 7 cm
Los Angeles County Museum of Art, gift of
John Gilbert Bourne, M.76.157

A ritual performer stands ready, holding his costume's substantial back rack adorned with birds. His wide collar, perhaps depicting one made of carved shell, and his sizeable pectoral hanging to his waist epitomize the multifaceted attire of Classic Maya ritual performers. The curious funnel-shaped object clutched in his right hand eludes identification although it resembles a kind of large trumpet seen in the spectacular Bonampak murals, which record a momentous public pageant.

The figure is colored with the pigment called Maya Blue. This vibrant paint, famed for its rare stability of hue, was discovered by the Maya prior to 200 BCE. Maya Blue is produced by combining palygorskite clay, found especially in small deposits in Yucatan, Mexico, with indigo, a plant-based pigment. The two ingredients are heated to ca. 150–200° C, which causes the indigo to become molecularly embedded (intercalcated) into the clay, thus making the blue color stable.[1] Not only does Maya Blue lend a striking color to artworks; it also was symbolic of sacredness, fertility, and the regeneration of life.

Note

1. Roundhill et al. 1994, 253–56.

86. DWARF FIGURINE

Maya, Campeche, Mexico or Guatemala
Late Classic Period, 550–850 CE
Earthenware, post-fire paint
20.3 × 12.7 × 15.9 cm
2009.20.36

Dwarfs were important members of royal Maya courts. They are portrayed serving food, playing musical instruments, holding sacred objects for the ruler, and as diviners and scribes. Their elevated social roles were steeped in cosmology and religious mythology, especially that of the maize god, who was assisted by a dwarf when the deity set the Three Stones of the cosmic hearth at the beginning of Creation.[1] The Classic Maya viewed dwarfs as the living embodiment of the maize god's supernatural helpers, who continued their sacred duty in the regal court. Maya peoples today believe that earlier creations were populated by a race of dwarfs who now reside inside the earth, living below the ruins of the ancient cities.

The ornate turban worn by this dwarf is typical of the courtly garb of key individuals serving the ruler. This so-called spangled turban headdress is especially connected to gods and humans associated with Creation and scribal duties.[2] A curious feature of this dwarf is what may be a halved cacao pod held in his right hand. His cheeks are covered with what appears to be a thin, woven fabric; this recalls other figurines, many of which are dwarfs, with an unidentifiable material plastered to the lower half of their face.[3] These features suggest the depiction of a formal rite. The graceful rendering of this figure and the exceptional attention to detail reveal the work of a master artist.

Notes

1. Looper, Reents-Budet, and Bishop 2009, 117–22.

2. Coe and Kerr 1998, 105.

3. Schele 1997, 156–57, pls. 10, 12.

87. FIGURAL PENDANT

Maya, Guatemala, Belize, Mexico or Honduras
Middle Classic Period, 450–650 CE
Jadeite[1]
6.7 × 4.2 × 0.8 cm
2009.20.6

88. FACE PENDANT

Maya, Guatemala, Belize, Mexico or Honduras
Late Classic Period, 650–850 CE
Jadeite, albite[1]
9.3 × 11.8 × 1.8 cm
2009.20.8

89. FIGURAL PENDANT

Maya, Guatemala, Belize, Mexico or Honduras
Early Classic Period, 250–450 CE
Jadeite[1]
6.86 × 4.83 × 1.27 cm
TL.2009.20.263

90. FIGURAL PENDANT

Maya, Guatemala, Belize, Mexico or Honduras
Early Classic Period, 250–450 CE
Jadeite,[1] red pigment
8.2 × 1.7 × 1.5 cm
TL.2009.20.232

91. NECKLACE WITH PENDANTS

Maya, Guatemala, Belize, Mexico or Honduras
Late Classic Period, 650–850 CE
Pendants: albite, omphacite, and jadeite[1]
Largest pendant: 5.7 × 4.4 × 1.9 cm;
necklace: length 78 cm
TL.2009.20.264

Jadeite is a dense alumina silicate of the pyroxene mineral family. The preferred stone for denoting status and sacredness throughout Mesoamerica, its value was based on its relative scarcity, the polished stone's bright, shiny surface, its translucent colors (ranging from light green to a rich blue-green), and the challenge of carving the stone due to the stone's hardness. In addition to the impressive visual qualities and scarcity, jadeite was symbolically linked to the miracle of the earth's fecundity, the maize god, and the life-giving promise of green plants and blue-green water. Together, these attributes made jadeite the most valuable of all materials to adorn the nobility and the gods. The Maya also fashioned adornments from similar green-colored stones whose visual properties resemble those of jadeite. It is difficult to discern the correct geological identification of these adornments without technical analyses.

These four pendants and necklace exemplify the aesthetic variety and technical expertise of Classic Maya jadeite carvers. The pendants are carved in the standardized frontal rendering of a noble person wearing the formal head gear of the ruling elite, yet each displays unique features that document more than five hundred years of the jadeite carver's art. The two flat pendants (nos. 87, 88) exemplify Middle and Late Classic figural pendant styles with the distinctive headdresses and impressive jadeite earflares and bead necklaces worn by the nobility. The Early Classic pendant (no. 89) is expertly carved from a small jadeite boulder, the artist deftly sculpting the irregularly shaped stone into an emotive figural artwork. The carver accentuated the earflares which serve as a frame for the figure's serene face as well as an overt sign of his high status. The nearly full-figural, elongated pendant (no. 90) is an unusual shape and type of portrayal for Classic Maya jadeite jewelry. It is further distinguished by the intense green color of the stone; the eye sockets may originally have held inlays of shell, iron pyrite or some other material to depict pupils. The necklace (no. 91) includes beads and exquisitely carved small plaques depicting lords whose guise recalls that of the Maize god.

Notes

1. Nondestructive Raman analysis was used to identify the stone. The analysis was carried out by Catherine Matsen, conservation scientist at the Scientific Research and Analysis Laboratory of the Winterthur Museum and Country Estate, Wilmington, Delaware.

92

93

92. STUCCO PORTRAIT HEAD

Maya, Campeche, Mexico

Late Classic Period, 550–850 CE

Stucco, paint

28 × 23.9 × 17.9 cm

2009.20.26

93. STUCCO PORTRAIT HEAD

Maya, Mexico, Belize or Guatemala

Late Classic Period, 550–850 CE

Stucco, paint

28.7 × 24.4 × 18.8 cm

2009.20.46

A fundamental feature of Mesoamerican formal architecture was the use of molded, modeled, and carved stucco decoration. Painted either monochrome red or in a variety of colors, these façades narrated key precepts of religio-political ideology, displaying the supernatural patrons and worldly authority of the aristocracy that used the structures. The façade decoration also could reveal a building's function as well as its symbolic identity.[1] These two stucco heads, which were part of a larger pictorial façade narrative, illustrate the close connection between the gods and Maya aristocracy. The head with intact earflares (no. 92) depicts the maize god, recognized by the *tau*-shaped tooth, sloping forehead, and tonsured hair. He is adorned with the abundant jadeite jewelry typical of renderings of the deity, including earflares and a tubular bead headband with a large, central diadem. The other head (no. 93) wears the same Maize

god headband, although here the tubular beads are indicated by paint rather than the modeled and painted ones of the other sculpture. The lack of *tau*-shaped tooth and more personalized facial features suggest the rendering of a member of the Classic Period elite.

The Maya would often intentionally destroy a building's decorative façade and then collapse the vaulted chambers prior to constructing a new building atop the rubble.[2] Frequently, the rubble contained fragments of the old stucco narrative now buried below the new platform. Most often it is the heads that survive in the debitage which suggests that the Maya paid particular attention to the faces of deities and royalty when they destroyed stucco façades during renovation projects. In addition, stucco façade heads have been found as offerings in tombs or other ritual caches placed inside buildings. Such special treatment indicates the prestige

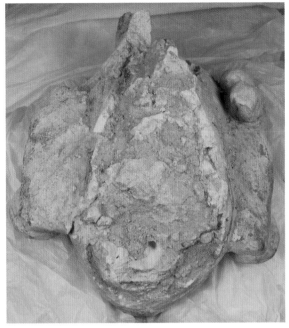

Fig. 1 (left). The cross section of a sample from no. 92 shows three layers: a fine white stucco base layer, a red pigment layer with fine red pigment particles, and an upper green layer, in which discrete pigment particles are difficult to discern. (125x, Nikon D70 digital camera, in reflected light on a Leitz Wetzlar polarized light microscope)

Fig. 2 (right). The reverse of no. 92 is a mass of rough, friable white stucco mixed with light tan dirt.

and likely perceived spiritual power of these stucco portraits among the Classic Period Maya.

Technical Commentary

The portrait head fragment (no. 92) is hand modeled from successive layers of fine, white stucco without any interior armature or substructure.[3] A small shell fragment was found embedded in the stucco.[4] The stucco surface is painted red and green; the face, ears, and sections of the back of the head are painted red, the headdress and earflares green. In some areas green paint overlaps onto the red layer, indicating that the red was applied first. Examination of a sample viewed in cross-section indicates that the paint layers were applied while the stucco was wet. This is demonstrated by the fact that the red paint layer permeates both the stucco and the green paint (fig. 1) (JA).

Notes

1. Fash 1991, 115–38. See also Boone 1985.

2. For an example of an intentionally preserved stucco-and-paint façade, see Agurcia Fasquelle 2005, 72–73.

3. Fourier-transform infrared spectroscopy performed by Glenn Gates at the Walters Art Museum identified calcium carbonate as a major component of the white stucco. Calcium carbonate, in the form of calcite, has previously been identified in Maya stucco using Raman spectroscopy and Fourier-transform infrared imaging with attenuated total reflection. Vandenabeele et al. 2005; Goodall 2008.

4. To produce stucco, the Maya burned limestone and shells to make quicklime, which was slaked with water to produce hydrated lime. Coe and Kerr 1998, 134.

94. BURIAL URN

K'iché Maya, Southern Highlands, Guatemala
Late Classic Period, 550–850 CE
Earthenware, post-fire paint
55.8 × 67.4 × 57.9 cm
2009.20.41

Large, lidded urns were unique to the K'iché Maya of southern Guatemala. The urns contained the remains of important individuals who either were placed in the urn as a tightly wrapped bundle or as a secondary burial of the remaining bones. A few have reportedly been found buried in the pyramidal platforms of ritual buildings, but the majority come from sacred caves where descendants would make pilgrimages to give offerings and seek advice from their revered ancestors.

The front of this urn is adorned with the image of what is likely an ancestor who, at death, was transformed into a spirit embodiment of a deity. This deity/ancestor combines features of K'inich Ajaw (the sun god) and GI, a patron god at Palenque, Mexico.[1]

He emerges from the open maw of the *xoc* (shark) saurian, which symbolizes the watery underworld, the deified personage ready to interact with his prayerful descendants. The special connection with the supernatural, and particularly with such deities as the maize god and K'inich Ajaw, was the ideological foundation of royal authority figures among the Maya, a Mesoamerican trait with its origins in the Formative Period among the Olmecs.[2]

Notes

1. Fort Worth 1986, 48.

2. Ibid., 301–7. See also Los Angeles 2005, 20–27

95. LIDDED VESSEL

Maya, Guatemala
Early Classic Period, 250–550 CE
Earthenware, slip, incising
Height 34.8 cm, diameter 22.9 cm
2009.20.39

The Classic Maya political landscape was divided into more than two dozen polities, similar to city-states, composed of a primary site plus aligned towns and villages. Each was headed by a royal lineage supported by noble families, and the polities often competed against each other for political and economic supremacy. Feasts sponsored by the ruling elite provided a crucial platform for securing relations among aligned parties and negotiating new alliances. Feasts were integral to elaborate affairs of state, from rulers' accession rites to royal weddings to war victory celebrations and special religious observances. The consumption of large amounts of sumptuous foods, including drinks made from highly valued cacao (chocolate), was a focal point. The banquets prompted the production of finely made food-service wares in the form of pictorial pottery, their decorative imagery often featuring themes lauding the earthly or supernatural prowess of the host. These ornate vessels also functioned as gifts, their acceptance signaling the guests' alliance or, at least, an association with the host.

The vase's hieroglyphic text confirms its function as a drinking vessel—*kakaw yuk'ib*, or "the cacao drinking cup of . . ."[1] The text goes on to name the cup's patron/owner (at B2) and his father (at D1–D2)[2] Chakjal Mukuuy, "Reddening Dove."[3] Neither of these individuals is known from other Early Classic hieroglyphic texts, and thus we do not know their political or familial identities. Yet the artistic quality of the vessel and its detailed nominal phrase indicate their being members of the nobility if not a royal dynasty of the fourth–fifth centuries.

The two hieroglyphic texts are separated by pictorial panels featuring the maize god as an embodied cacao tree.[4] His bejeweled headdress is topped by a sprouting cacao tree like those adorning the vase's lid. Modeled cacao pods embellish the vessel, and the lid's knob is a cacao tree with a bird (now broken). The avian may be the false sun of the previous creation and avatar of the deity Itz'amnaj (God D).[5] Uniting text and image panels are overlapping bands of cacao leaves. The preponderance of cacao imagery supports the interpretation of the text's unusual introductory glyphs (A1–B1) as "sprouting cacao," based on the first sign's resemblance to the vase's sprouting trees (see the Maize god's headdress) and its sub-fixed sign -la, a well-known adjectival element in Maya hieroglyphic writing (MZ / DR-B).[6]

Notes

1. Stuart 2007, 184–201.

2. A third person may be named in the text, the glyph compound at C2 perhaps being a second relationship glyph given its initial u- ("his/her"). However, the undeciphered main sign complicates the matter. It is not uncommon to have both a father and mother named in such parentage phrases. Yet the glyph in question may simply be the continuation of the father's name.

3. Houston et al. 2009; Houston, Robertson, and Stuart 2001.

4. Martin 2007.

5. M. Miller and Taube 1993, 99–100; Bassie 2002.

6. David Stuart (2007, 199–201) describes a very similar "sprouting of cacao" in the text on an elaborate jade mosaic vessel from the royal Burial 116 at Tikal.

A   B

Transcription	Translation	Transcription	Translation
A1 ?-la	tzi, ja, la (sprouting [?])	B1 ka2-wa	kakaw (cacao [chocolate])
A2 yu-k'i-bi	yuk'ib (his/her drinking cup)	B2 ?-IK'	?- IK' (wind [an early form of the glyph])

Transcription	Translation	Transcription	Translation
CI u-MIJIN	umijin (his father)	DI ?	TI', CHAK, AJAW (?) [father's name]
C2 u-?-li		D2 CHAK-ja-la-mu-ku-yi	chakjal mukuuy (Reddening Dove)

Loose translation

"Sprouting Cacao is the (name of the) drinking cup of . . . Ik', son of . . . , . . . Chakjal Mukuuy."

96. CYLINDER VASE

Maya, Petén Lowlands, Guatemala

Late Classic Period, 650–800 CE

Earthenware, slip paint

Height 22.1 cm, diameter 14.7 cm

TL.2009.20.177

Three of the most prominent shamanic transformation spirits decorate this drinking vessel. Such pictorial programs featuring spirit companions frequently include short hieroglyphic phrases that name each being, the phrase beginning with the glyph *u-way* "his nagual/animal spirit companion," followed by the being's name.[1] Although no such texts are found on this vase, other vessels' imagery records the name of the jaguar figure (A) as *tzuk-ch'ok? hix* "enema jaguar." The second *way* (B) seems to be a variant of the "Enema God A-Prime" being because here he appears to hold an enema bag in his extended arm. The third *way* (C) is the . . .

chih "deer-monkey" entity which frequently wears a wide collar adorned with eyeballs. All three beings have connections to the use of enemas by shamans to ingest psychoactive substances to assist their spiritual transformation.

The painter of this vase used rich red slip paint, expertly manipulating the pigment-loaded brush to produce a varied hue intensity to accentuate select areas. Such fine technique also draws our attention to the inherent visual qualities of water-based slip paints which further highlights the artist's sophisticated aesthetic practice. Of special note is the gray slip that embellishes such

items as the figures' wrist and ankle bands, the quetzal bird feathers in their costumes, the jaguar's water lily flower atop its head, and the jars filled with the enema concoction. This unique slip was originally green, and Classic Maya painters used it to color precious objects—here jadeite jewelry, quetzal feathers, the enema jars, and the spirit beings themselves.

Note

1. Grube and Nahm 1994.

A   B   C

97

97. GOURD-SHAPED BOWL

Maya, Campeche, Mexico
Middle Classic Period, 450–650 CE
Earthenware, burnished slip, incising
Height 11.4 cm, diameter 13.5 cm
TL.2009.20.274

98. BOWL

Maya, Campeche, Mexico
Late Classic Period, 550–850 CE
Earthenware, slip paint
Height 16 cm, diameter 16.5 cm
2009.20.30

The shape of these vessels makes reference to the gourd which was, and remains today, the primary food-service and drinking container among the Maya and other Mesoamerican peoples. The carved bowl (no. 97) is particularly reminiscent of a gourd in both its shape and decoration. The carving of gourds was the primary mode for embellishing these natural vessels, although painted stucco also was a known technique. The bowl's imagery features a saurian head with large eye curl and supra-orbital plate.

The painted bowl (no. 98) is decorated with four seated human figures. The black body-painting of some and the black spots on others suggest a supernatural identity or association for the group. The moderately abstract, elongated hand gestures are narrative signals which likely specify the nature of the interaction among the individuals. For

example, the seated figure with three black spots on his torso and arm strikes a pose that may connote a generalized greeting.[1] Yet in spite of detailed studies of pose and gesture in Maya art, the lack of corroborating evidence in the art historical, archaeological and ethno-historic records continues to challenge all efforts to ascertain the true meanings of these formalized gestures.[2]

Notes

1. Ancona-Ha, Pérez De Lara, and Van Stone 2000, 1080.

2. V. E. Miller 1981. See also Ancona-Ha, Pérez De Lara, and Van Stone 2000, 1072–83.

98

NICARAGUA

L. Nicaragua

• Ometepe

Gulf of
Papagayo

GREATER
NICOYA

ATLANTIC
WATERSHED

Caribbean Sea

COSTA
RICA

DIQUÍS

VERAGUAS-
GRAN CHIRIQUÍ

COCLÉ

PANAMA

• Conté

MACARACAS

PACIFIC OCEAN

CENTRAL AMERICA

TAIRONA

ZENÚ

COLOMBIA

CENTRAL AMERICA

On his fourth and last voyage, Christopher Columbus sailed southward along the eastern seaboard of Central America. In 1502 he encountered a land filled with many rivers, lush forests, dramatic mountains, and fertile valleys. His letter to the Spanish king described affable people who welcomed him with food and gold ornaments. In this first European ethnographic account of Costa Rica, Columbus was fixated on the large numbers of beautiful golden adornments worn by the native people while also remarking on their intelligence and friendliness. Due to the quantities of gold adornments, the Spanish named this region Costa Rica, the "Rich Coast."[1]

Although the Spanish admired the fine gold objects and the openness of the populace, they were blind to the region's environmental riches, which have spawned the modern ecotourism industry, with Costa Rica being a world leader in this arena. Similarly, Central America's archaeological riches have gone relatively unrecognized in part because the region is sandwiched between the two spectacular culture zones of Mesoamerica and Andean South America, which have long eclipsed the intermediate area. As a result, investigations have typically focused north or south and have failed to properly credit Central America's unique contributions to world art and cultural history.

Ancient Costa Rica is renowned for its exceptional carvings in jadeite, painted and modeled pottery, large figural stone sculptures, and exuberant golden body adornments. The country is divided into three archaeological regions based on natural geography that, to some degree, affected human developments such that the natural segmentations coincide with ancient cultural divisions. They include the Greater Nicoya zone, the Atlantic Watershed and Central Highlands region, and the Diquís zone, which spills over into neighboring Panama.

Artistic developments during the earliest phase (500 BCE–500 CE) coincided with social, political, and economic advancements. Finely modeled human effigy ceramics and expertly carved jadeite (and other green stone) adornments dominate the artistic landscape. Equally notable are the large and fancifully carved stone metates, which functioned as ceremonial seats and funerary biers and symbolized power over natural forces. Artworks frequently include animal imagery, especially the bat, various raptors, and the jaguar, often combined with human features. Such patterns of imagery point to shamanism as a key precept of Central American religion. Certain animals also probably served as clan totems, an interpretation based on their similar use among the Bribris, Muetares, Terrabas, and other native peoples of modern Costa Rica. At this time, too, similarities in artistic forms and iconographic traditions as well as actual objects imported from Mesoamerica indicate contact between these two great culture areas.

A dramatic shift took place soon after 500 CE, when jadeite was replaced by gold as the medium of choice for fashioning objects of personal use to denote social status. Knowledge of metallurgy most likely was introduced from Panama and Colombia and points southward. Connections with Mesoamerica ceased, as the imposing Teotihuacan culture of highland Mexico collapsed (around 650 CE) and caused major socioeconomic disruptions as far south as Costa Rica. The peoples of Central America searched elsewhere for opportunities, now favoring contacts with cultures in Andean South America. The golden objects created by Central American artists shared production techniques and iconographic forms with those of the gold-producing societies of Colombia and Ecuador, although the artists imbued their creations with many unique features.

Panama shares with Costa Rica the lack of extensive archaeological investigations, with a few exceptions. Archaeologists and art historians are reversing the long-held perception of ancient Panama as a cultural and artistic stepchild, recognizing it as a vital region with its own social traditions, religious ideologies, sociopolitical systems, and unique artistic expressions.

The cultures of ancient Panama are renowned for their precious metal and painted ceramic artworks, which are among the most vibrant articulations in these two media ever created in the ancient Americas. The technical skills evident in these objects, especially the fantastical golden adornments, speak of highly developed traditions that transferred from one generation of artists to the next their accumulated practical knowledge and creative spirit. Yet the Panamanian traditions also proffered sufficient creative latitude, which nourished experimentation and the invention of new expressions.

Panamanian art is particularly rich in an iconographic system that strives to represent the unrepresentable—that is, the world of dreams, shamanic transformation, and the supernatural within the natural. The scant ethno-historic data and paucity of ethnographic studies focusing on Panama's indigenous cultures hinder our ability to decode and comprehend the esoteric knowledge and religious beliefs exemplified by these artworks. Yet data from such modern native peoples as the San Blas and Bribri provide important clues concerning what metaphors may be pertinent to interpreting the ancient imagery created by their ancestors. All too frequently, however, a study of ancient Panamanian art generates more questions than answers. At the least, Panama's archaeological and artistic remains speak of highly developed societies with complex social, political, economic, and ideological systems and a long-standing creative tradition in the visual arts.

Note

1. Bray 1981.

99. SEATED PORTLY FIGURE

Atlantic Watershed, Costa Rica

Period VI, 1000–1550 CE

Earthenware, slip paint

21.1 × 15.2 × 16.5 cm

TL.2009.20.206

Large, figural ceramic portrayals are rare in the artistic history of the Atlantic Watershed region, the later centuries typified instead by large-scale stone sculptures. The identity of this seated portly figure is somewhat ambiguous; he may be a chief or other powerful individual, suggested by the stool-like sphere upon which he sits. This recalls the contemporaneous throne-seats or low, circular tables that are typical of the region at this time.[1] Alternatively, the tiny gourd held to his nostrils may indicate his ingestion of mind-altering snuff, and thus suggest the portrayal of a shaman. Shamanism is a spiritual belief found throughout the world.[2] Its central principle holds that every human being has a spirit companion, but only those with specially honed abilities are able to know their spirit form. These special individuals can transform themselves into their companion spirits, harness their supernatural powers, and wield these potent forces on earth— to cure illness, foretell the future, or ensure success on the battlefield. The shaman's transformational process is aided by such activities as meditative ritual pose, dance and music, and sensory deprivation. Often, too, it was assisted by the ingestion of mind-altering substances, from tobacco to alcohol to psychotropic plants and even the controlled use of animal poisons, frequently consumed in snuff form.

Often spirit companions take the form of powerful animals such as the jaguar and vulture. Others are zoomorphs whose natural life cycle includes a physical transformation such as the frog, which changes from a water-bound fish (a tadpole) to a terrestrial being. If this sculpture depicts a shaman, the fact that the figure retains his human attributes may imply a pre-transformation portrayal.

Notes

1. Detroit 1981, 215.

2. Stone-Miller 2002b, xv–xxvi.

100. EFFIGY METATE
(GRINDING STONE)

Atlantic Watershed, Costa Rica

Late Period V–Period VI, 700–1550 CE

Volcanic stone

9.8 × 21.8 × 15.9 cm

TL.2009.20.171

In 1502, the Spanish observed monolithic carved "boards" being used as funeral biers, their animal imagery identified as clan symbols. Other early accounts mention the use of similar but smaller "tables" to grind tobacco and other hallucinogenic materials used during shamanic religious rituals. Spanish missionaries destroyed many of these stone artworks because of their association with "pagan" rites. Equally unfortunate is the lack of descriptions by the early chroniclers of indigenous religious beliefs and myths as well as the dramatic population decline due to European diseases to which the native peoples had no natural immunity. As a result, little has survived to illuminate the religious and social beliefs of the societies of ancient Costa Rica. The paucity of data severely hinders our ability to interpret the meanings of the imagery in all media including these carved "grinding stones" which seemingly were key objects of ritual use throughout the region.

This small metate, or grinding stone, is carved in the form of a feline, its geometric designs recalling a jaguar's patterning while simultaneously making reference to decorated cloth. As such, this rendering can be interpreted as the portrayal of a shaman in his animal spirit form. The predominant hunter in the American forest, the jaguar is a foe to all living beings. Its ability to traverse earth's three main environments—from climbing trees to swimming through deep water to living in caves—and its seemingly magical capacity to hunt in the darkness of night make the jaguar a formidable spirit companion.

101. CAPTIVE FIGURE

Atlantic Watershed, Costa Rica
Late Period V–early Period VI, 900–1200 CE
Volcanic stone
44.2 × 24.9 × 12.7 cm
TL.2009.20.207

Warfare was a common means of territorial defense and expansion, the victors gaining land and resources and especially tribute in the form of goods (foodstuffs and crafted items) and human labor. The public display of bound captives proclaimed a community's hegemony and the prowess of the local chief, their communal dominance being preserved in the form of stone sculptures exhibited in plazas and around administrative/ceremonial buildings. The largest such sculptures are those of warriors, typically portrayed with raised weapon and carrying a trophy head. Smaller sculptures depict the vanquished such as this defeated warrior with bound arms above his head and ankles similarly secured. His midsection sports a beltlike wrapping adorned with shell or metal beads. The figure's pierced earlobes may have been garnished with ornaments, likely made of shell or metal.

102. TRIPOD DISH

Atlantic Watershed, Costa Rica

Period IV, 1–500 CE

Earthenware, slip paint, incising

31.2 × 26 × 25.1 cm

TL.2009.20.208

The Ticabán style of pottery from the Atlantic Watershed of east-central Costa Rica is characterized by modeling rather than painting to create pictorial forms.[1] Throughout most of Costa Rica and southern Nicaragua during the first half of the first millennium CE, painted imagery was the dominant approach to ceramic embellishment. The best works in the Ticabán style combine a sensuous smoothness of the pottery surface with elegantly shaped vessels and dynamic zoomorphic supports and embellishments. Often these are made of solid clay; the vessels not exploding during the firing process indicates the high degree of technical skill of the region's ancient ceramicists.

This dish's tall supports are modeled in the form of a human-owl composite being, perhaps a shamanic entity. The artist harmonized dynamic modeling and delicate punctated areas with the supplely smoothed surface that dominates the vessel. Sparse use of paint accentuates the zoomorphic shapes of the supports. The graceful flare of the vessel's rim adroitly balances the visual heaviness of the substantial zoomorphic supports.

Note

1. Stone-Miller 2002b, 120–24.

103. HUMAN EFFIGY PENDANT

Diquís, Costa Rica

Late Period IV–Period VI, 400–1500 CE

Cast gold alloy

14.6 × 10.5 × 3 cm

TL.2009.20.74

After 500 CE, gold became the dominant medium for fashioning personal adornments. Bracelets, effigy pendants, and large pectorals and headbands were decorated with geometric motifs and cast in the shape of animals and shamanic spirit forms. Goldsmiths in southwestern Costa Rica perfected the lost-wax casting technique introduced from Colombia sometime after 300 CE. Diquís artisans produced individualistic styles expressing local beliefs while sharing pictorial narratives and pectoral forms with societies throughout the region, especially the Chiriquí of adjacent western Panama. The elaborate figural pendants include representations of shamans in their animal spirit forms, sometimes depicted dancing and playing instruments during the transformational rites.

This figural pendant features a performer playing a small drum, held in his right hand, and a flute rendered as a serpent and held to his mouth. The figure's bent knees imply dance, a common element of shamanic transformation rituals. His spiritual state is signified by the two serpent-spirits emanating from his head, the center of identity, and by the saurian heads emerging from his shoulders and knees. The shaman's round ears and wide, narrow mouth may reveal his spirit form as that of a bat.

Technical Commentary

The pendant is an open-backed, lost-wax casting, cast in a single piece from an alloy (determined by X-ray fluorescence) of Au 69.5%, Cu 26.6%, Ag 2.6%. This alloy composition is comparable to published

Fig. 1. The back of no. 103, showing a rectangular tab used to attach decorative elements.

XRF data on cast-gold Diquís objects from ancient Costa Rica.[1] Porosity from casting is visible in the x-ray image in areas of the figure's arms, legs, and feet. Areas have been left unfinished, especially underneath and inside the drum, where the metal has a sandy texture. Its overall copper color reflects the high copper content, but originally it had a gold-enriched surface subsequently abraded by polishing. The figure's feet were worked after casting to achieve their flattened, triangular shape, and as a result there are numerous stress-cracks visible along their edges. On the back of the object, there is a

single, cast-in ring at the figure's neck; rectangular tabs (partially visible) were used to attach various elements (fig. 1).

There is no evidence of major repairs. Minor casting flaws are present in three of the eight false filigree spirals along the upper edge of the figure's headdress. There is no corrosion present on the object (JA).

Notes

1. D. Scott 1994, 502.

104. RAPTORIAL BIRD (FALCON?) EFFIGY VESSEL

Papagayo Polychrome, Greater Nicoya,
Nicaragua/Costa Rica
Period VI, 1000–1350 CE
Earthenware, white slip overall with
painted decoration
30.5 × 18.3 × 22.4 cm
TL.2009.20.282

This masterful portrayal of a shaman's raptorial bird spirit form relies on a skillful integration of modeling and painting to achieve a convincing composition. The bird's head, including the raptor's deadly pointed beak, and the tips of its wings and tail are indicated by modeled flanges. The artist then painted details of wing and tail feathers as panels extending below the modeled forms to complete their renderings. The painted design on the vessel's pedestal support mimics the painted wings, thereby accentuating the avian identity of the effigy vessel.

The sides of this extraordinary vessel are each painted with a human form. Their skillful integration into the bird's body reveals the true significance of the vessel as the depiction of a shaman's spirit form. Each of the two figures grasps a staff surmounted by a human skull, the staff perhaps making reference to the shaman's spiritual transformation being likened to death and rebirth.

The burning of incense was an important part of myriad rituals throughout Mesoamerica and Central America. Smoke served to alternatively screen and reveal the activities of the sacred rite, the magical smoke being present and suddenly disappearing as it rises to the heavens. The incense, typically pungent copal from a pine tree, stimulated the participants' olfactory sense. Together, the smoke's effects call to mind the ethereal world of the supernatural.[1]

This incense burner is topped with the portrayal of a caiman or other member of the Crocodylidae family, one of the frequent animal spirit forms of Central American shamans. Its particularly aggressive stance may refer to the practitioner's battle against supernatural forces. Many such incense burners were found ritually broken on the slopes of a principal volcano on the island of Ometepe in Lake Nicaragua, the incense burner lid with its smoke issuing from the top mimicking an active volcano. Among peoples from southern Nicaragua to Mesoamerica the earth was likened to the back of a crocodile floating in the primordial sea, its dorsal scutes being the volcanic north–south backbone that defines the continents of the Western Hemisphere. This incense burner, then, constitutes a profound ritual vessel pertaining to the transition from the natural to the supernatural realms and a symbolic model of the ancient Costa Rican world.

Note

1. Stone-Miller 2002b, 90–92.

105. CROCODILE EFFIGY INCENSE BURNER

Potosí Appliqué, Greater Nicoya, Costa Rica

Periods V–VI, 500–1350 CE

Earthenware, traces of white ground

60.1 × 32 × 31.9 cm

2009.20.45

106. PEDESTAL DISH

Joaquín Polychrome, Central Panama

600–800 CE

Earthenware, slip paint

Height 15.2 cm, diameter 27.7 cm

TL.2009.20.205

107. PEDESTAL BOWL

Macaracas, Central Panama

800–1000 CE

Earthenware, white slip, slip paint (black, red)

Height 26.7 cm, diameter 19.3 cm

TL.2009.20.204

Binary opposition is a central precept of ancient Panamanian cosmology, which viewed the cosmos as the pairing of opposites: male-female, light-dark, spirit world-natural world. The universe was composed of three levels—the upper sphere, the middle sphere, and the lower sphere. The latter was associated with the female domain and was mirrored in the upper sphere, the domain of the male principle. Decorative motifs, especially certain geometric forms frequently found on painted ceramics, likely had symbolic meanings, although their significance has largely been lost. Perhaps, too, some forms encompassed esoteric knowledge that was not intended for the uninitiated. Regardless, the dynamic imagery that characterizes the Conté and Marcaracas pottery styles is cognitive in its intent and likely reflects fundamental principles of indigenous religious beliefs and cosmology.[1]

The pedestal dish (no. 106) is decorated with a bilaterally symmetrical portrayal of a shaman in magical flight. Having taken his animal spirit form, here a bat, the shaman's ability to traverse the cosmic realms is implied by his portrayal in mirror image. Only a hint of the shaman's human self remains in his face; otherwise the transformation into a bat is complete with outstretched, featherless wings, and sinuous clawed feet.

The pedestal bowl (no. 107) joins a round bowl with a pedestal support. Macaracas wares are characterized by dramatic, geometric motifs that have symbolic meanings pertaining to universal models, spirit forces, and related archetypal phenomena. Here the artist's use of strong black, deep red, and purple slip colors separated by a rich beige hue intensifies the visual energy of the design program.

Note

1. Labbé 1992.

106

107

Gold adornments covered the cloth-wrapped bodies of ancient Panamanian chiefs, as described by Spanish explorers in 1519 who witnessed the funeral of one such leader. The adornments included scores of disks of cold-hammered sheet gold, many adorned with embossed images of shamans transformed into their spirit forms. Their spiritual transformation is symbolized by the composite human-animal being, often combining jaguar, caiman, or raptorial bird forms, with vibrant emanations rendering their supernatural powers.

This pectoral disk presents an atypical rendering of the transformed being. Uncharacteristic Coclé canons of representation are the open mouth with only one row of teeth, the round rather than oval-shaped eyes, nostrils closed at the bottom and abutting the mouth, and the well-defined visual separation of the figure from his spirit emanations and the background. The belt ties/emanations below the upraised arms are not rendered as serpent-caiman forms which is usual for this type of Coclé pectoral. Other unusual or unique features are the border around the disk's edge and the four pairs of punched tie-holes rather than the typical two pairs.

Close examination of the piece reveals light scratches over the entire surface of the disk. Fine and uniform polishing marks exhibit no variability, unlike those of hand-polishing as is typical of Coclé workmanship. Uncharacteristic file marks also are visible on the proper left shoulder of the figure, and the punched tie-holes are very circular rather than irregular as seen on other Coclé disk pendants. The minimal surface accretions on the front and back can be easily removed.

108. SHAMAN EFFIGY PENDANT

Coclé style, Panama
Gold alloy
13.6 × 14.2 × 0.3 cm
Courtesy of the New Mexico History Museum, History Collections, gift of John Bourne, 11372.45

109. FROG EFFIGY PENDANT

Veraguas-Gran Chiriquí or Coclé, Panama

Periods V–VI, 700–1520 CE

Cast gold alloy

11.9 × 9.6 × 3.5 cm

TL.2009.20.250

110. NECKLACE WITH SHAMANIC EFFIGY PENDANT

Veraguas-Gran Chiriquí,

Veraguas Province, Panama

Periods V–VI, 700–1520 CE

Pendant: cast gold alloy

Pendant: 8.8 × 6.9 × 2 cm;

necklace: length 60.5 cm

TL.2009.20.86

111. SHAMANIC EFFIGY PENDANT

Coclé, Zenú, or Tairona, Panama or Colombia

700–1520 CE

Cast gold alloy

5.3 × 8.6 × 4.8 cm

TL.2009.20.81

Sometime after 500 CE, gold became the preferred material for fashioning personal adornments, supplanting jadeite and other green stones from which artists had made impressive pendants and necklaces for centuries. The relatively sudden appearance of gold and the specialized knowledge needed to work it imply the introduction of metallurgy from outside the region. All evidence points to northwestern Colombia as the point of origin of the metal arts, a region filled with other archaeological and art historical lines of evidence indicating a long-standing history of contacts between the two regions.

Gold pendants were cast in a variety of forms, from relatively naturalistic portrayals of animals to composite creatures combining human and zoomorphic features. The frog may be a totem (no. 109), symbolic of transformational abilities or special connections to the supernatural. The two shamanic effigy pendants portray supra-natural entities composed of a variety of zoomorphic body forms. The pendant (no. 110) is formed from a tortoise's body with crocodile-like legs and a bifurcated tail, the latter element symbolizing shamanic power.[1] The curly-tailed animal pendant (no. 111) represents a type found from eastern Panama to the coastal regions of the Zenú and Tairona cultures of northern Colombia. This "international style" adornment combines a crested bird's head with a feline's body and a serpent's tail. The front paws curl in on themselves to form suspension tubes. The composite creature format was developed by artists throughout the ancient Americas to portray the non-portrayable—the shaman transformed into his/her spirit form.[2] As such, all three golden adornments would have been potent totemic icons for a family or social group, intimating the members' special powers.

Technical Commentary

No. 109: Lost-wax cast in a single pour, this gold alloy frog shows evidence of difficulty with the casting. Areas of thin metal and greater porosity visible near the loss beneath the front right leg reflect problems achieving a continuous flow of metal throughout the mold (fig. 1). The crack across the middle of the frog's body is also related to initial problems in the cast, and an elongated patch of increased density near the top of the right leg is the location of an original cast-on repair. The reverse of the head, arms, and torso are hollow; the as-cast surface reflects the texture of the original core material (fig. 2). The concentration of air bubbles in the feet indicates that the frog was cast head down (fig. 1).[3] The flat feet may have been additionally thinned and shaped by hammering after casting.

Cast from a *tumbaga* alloy of 71.5% gold, 27.3% copper, 1% silver, the object represents the intentional alloying of copper and gold.[4] At this low percentage, however, the silver was likely introduced from sources of alluvial on placer gold and was not an intentional addition.[5] The relatively high gold content and low silver content has been observed in other examples of tumbaga from this region in Panama.[6] The coppery colored surface may indicate that there was little or no intentional surface enrichment of gold. In fact, the coppery color noted on many frog pendants from this region may be of some significance (JL).

No. 110: The pendant is hollow lost-wax cast from a high-purity gold alloy (Au 82.3%, Cu 10.2%, Ag 5.6%, reported here as average weight percent), which has been depletion gilded.[7] Though the copper content is likely a deliberate addition, the low percentage of

109

110

111

silver may be a result of the use of alluvial gold sources, which contain silver.[8] Overall, its composition is consistent with alloys of related examples from Panama.[9] Casting cores were used to create separate hollow cavities for the head and torso, and remnants of a red core material remain in the head. The extended beak and raised areas on the underside of the feet may be part of the original casting system. Arteries originally in wax, then cast into metal, were used to introduce molten metal into the mold.

The reverse is essentially flat, and the pendant would have been suspended by two hanging loops at the top, both of which display evidence of wear consistent with the object's use as a pendant (fig. 3). There is no significant corrosion (JL).

No. 111: Though clearly cast,[10] this figurine is lighter and thinner than the two pendants illustrated here. Wax ribbons spiraled upon themselves were used to create the cast-in-place headdress on this shamanic figure. A wax model was created over a fully formed core, leaving the figure open at the bottom. Examination and analysis confirm that the pendant is hollow-cast in a single pour from a high-purity gold alloy, Au 76.3%, Cu 16.9%, Ag 6.6% that has been depletion gilded. A copper-colored alloy is visible beneath the gold enriched surface along well-worn areas of the eyes and front paws.

Evidence of difficulty with the pour can be seen in the porosities and subsequent breakage visible in the x-radiograph (fig. 4). The interior is covered with a dark red earthen material that may be remnants of a casting core left in place to support this fragile form. A pair of holes seen in the x-ray image near the front feet indicates the position of a pin used to hold the core in place during casting. A small round cast-in repair at the front of the chest indicates that some working after casting was necessary.

While the copper content of this piece is not unusually high,[11] the pendant is heavily corroded and has multiple breaks (JL).

Notes

1. Labbé 1995, 139, no. 102b.

2. Ibid., 105–7.

3. Because gases rise while the molten metal cools, the concentration of air bubbles in the feet may indicate the direction of pouring during casting.

4. This piece falls well within other cited examples from Costa Rica and Panama analyzed by David Scott (1994, 502, table 2).

5. Harrison and Beaubien 2010, 202. See also D. Scott 1994, 510.

6. Harrison and Beaubien 2010, 202.

7. David Scott found experimentally that the elemental variation between surface and substrate of tumbaga alloys was only a few percentage points difference. Therefore we are using surface analysis as representative of the gold alloy matrix overall. D. Scott 1994, 504.

8. Ibid., 510. Scott reports here the XRF analysis of two gold nuggets from Costa Rica containing up to 2.8% silver. See also Harrison and Beaubien 2010, 200–202 for a discussion of the silver content as impurity in gold ranging up to 8%.

9. Ibid., 198–203.

10. A dendritic structure typical of cast metal alloys is visible on the tail of this figure.

11. This piece falls well within the range of copper content found in Panamanian gold, which frequently occurs in levels of 30–40%. See D. Scott 1994, 502, table 2.

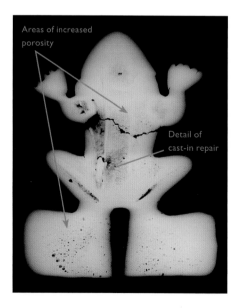

Fig. 1. No. 109: X-radiograph. The digital x-ray image was captured and viewed using GE Inspection Technologies' digital x-ray scanner and software.

Fig. 2. No. 109: Reverse

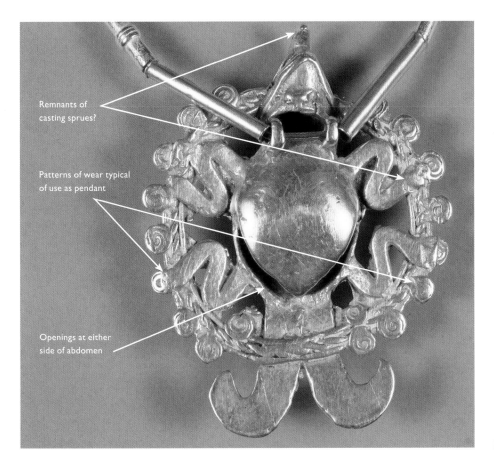

Remnants of casting sprues?

Patterns of wear typical of use as pendant

Openings at either side of abdomen

Fig. 3. No. 110: reverse

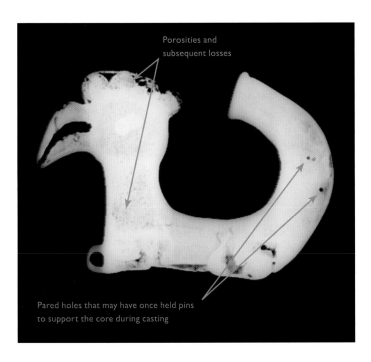

Porosities and subsequent losses

Pared holes that may have once held pins to support the core during casting

Fig. 4. No. 111: x-ray image. The digital x-ray image was captured and viewed with GE Inspection Technologies' x-ray scanner and software.

Fig. 5. No. 111: underside

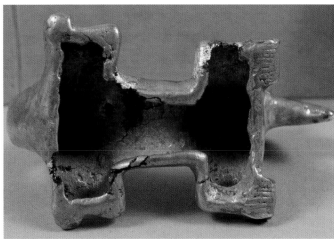

ANDEAN SOUTH AMERICA

COLOMBIA & ECUADOR

The present-day countries of Colombia and Ecuador geographically bridge the ancient societies of Central America and those of Peru and Bolivia. Yet they should not be viewed as a unitary, ancient culture area connecting the two other regions. Instead, the indigenous peoples of Colombia and Ecuador comprised highly varied societies, each distinctive in its sociopolitical, spiritual, and artistic expressions. It is true that these societies were often in contact with each other as well as with cultures to the north and south, their interactions preserved in common features of architecture, artistic forms, and symbolic iconography. In particular, they share the use of sumptuous, golden body adornments and the custom of lavishly furnished shaft tombs for the honored dead. Yet their individual uniqueness is reflected in novel artistic remains, from ceramics to stone sculptures to works in precious metals. These creations exemplify idiosyncratic solutions to the challenges of creating appropriate material expressions that embody the fundamental needs and aspirations of each society.

The region's rich, volcanic soils, plentiful rainfall, temperate climates, highland and lowland eco-zones, and the abundance of foods and materials from the Pacific Ocean supported emerging populations as early as 4000 BCE. Even 5,400 years later, the Inka empire coveted these resources, having expanded northward from southern Peru during the late fifteenth century. They had gained control of most of Ecuador and were extending their influence into southern Colombia when the Spanish arrived in the early sixteenth century.

Spanish interest in the region was focused on the large amount of gold artifacts they found in use among the native populations. They extracted every piece of the precious metal they could find and melted the objects into gold ingots to enrich the coffers of the Spanish Crown and the Catholic Church. They paid little attention to the fine workmanship or the complex symbolic meanings of these precious metal creations. For the Spanish, gold portended personal, imperial and ecclesiastical dominance, whereas among most peoples of Colombia, gold embodied the power of the sun, a divine force. Among the Muisca and Guane societies of the eastern Cordillera of Colombia, gold was part of a complex ideology of binary oppositions (male-female, light-dark, earth world-spirit world). The imagery on their gold ornaments pertains to this spiritual cosmology as well as to societal structure and humanity's place in the universe.

The technical repertoire of the Colombian and Ecuadorian goldsmiths included lost-wax and stone-mold casting, soldering, and cold-hammering to produce thin sheets of gold. A variety of surface manipulation techniques, such as embossing and depletion gilding, provided additional methods for producing impressive objects. Being masters of process and design, the ancient Colombian and Ecuadorian artists created wonders of form and symbolism in gold, copper, platinum, and, to a lesser extent, silver. Their counterparts' abilities to manipulate clay, stone, and other materials into fine works of art is less well known today but nonetheless technically impressive and aesthetically expressive.

112. BURIAL URN

Chimila, Magdalena-César region, Colombia
1000–1500 CE
Earthenware
49.6 × 26.9 × 27.4 cm
TL.2009.20.214

Figural urns found in chambers inside deep shaft tombs are particularly abundant in northwestern Colombia. The urns contained human bones, redeposited in these special containers after the flesh was removed either through cremation or burial in the ground for a short period of time. The shaft tomb burials were believed to be vital links to the honored dead, and the bones were perceived as seeds from which new life sprang. The practice of redepositing the defleshed skeletal remains inside urns and placing them in shaft tombs reenacted this ideology. By "planting" bones (seeds) in phallus-shaped urns inside womblike chambers in the ground (mother earth), renewed life would spring from the burials. A related belief concerning the nature of the tomb has been recorded among the present-day Desana people of northern Colombia. They define the grave as a uterus to which the physical part of all humans returns at death.[1]

Note

1. Santa Ana 1986, 115–16.

113. BURIAL URN

Moskito, lower Magdalena
River region, Colombia
1000–1600 CE
Eathenware, trace of white ground and
yellow pigment
74.4 × 32.9 × 26 cm
TL.2009.20.215

The burial-urn style of the lower Magdalena
River region of northern Colombia is
renowned for its figural portrayals of a male
personage sitting atop a low bench that
adorn the urns' lids. Often birds, as totemic
or otherwise symbolic icons, embellish the
urns' sides. The modeled male figure atop
the lid typically is portrayed nude, although
occasionally he may be ornamented with a
necklace or other body decoration. Here,
the pierced earlobes indicate that the figure
originally wore some type of ear ornament.
The ornamentation of burial urns with all
manner of modeled embellishments, be they
figural or more abstract, recalls the sixteenth-
century Spanish chronicler Pedro de Aguado,
who described the bones and ashes of a
cremated chief having been placed in a clay
vessel that then was garnished with jewels
and other finery.[1]

Note

1. Santa Ana 1986, 11.

114. SOLAR EFFIGY OCARINA

Tairona, Sierra Nevada de Santa
Marta region, Colombia
1000–1550 CE
Burnished earthenware, incising
10.8 × 10.2 × 3.2 cm
TL.2009.20.227

Among the modern descendants of the Tairona archaeological culture, the Kogi believe the sun resides in a sky-house where it sits on a bench and chews coca, sometimes being portrayed with an extruding tongue. They associate the jaguar with the sun, and view the solar "being" as both a progenitor and a devourer. Kogi religion is focused on the need to maintain a balance among all things physical and spiritual, a concept reflected in the Kogi's model of a nine-level universe. Humanity resides in the middle—the fifth level—with four benevolent levels above and four malevolent levels below.

A rich and varied tradition of performance rituals was developed to help maintain the ideal community in harmony with the natural, balanced order of the universe. The playing of musical instruments was integral to these performances. Certain sounds likely held symbolic meaning, although the Spanish massacre of the region's ruling families in the sixteenth century and the rapid native population decline caused by disease and despair destroyed much of the ritual life and spiritual beliefs of the Tairona.

This ocarina is a multi-toned whistle with four finger holes on the front and the mouthpiece at the top of the figure. The personage may represent an aspect of the solar deity with his characteristic protruding tongue, rayed headdress, and double-headed caiman bench. Frequently, this type of black-slipped ocarina has fugitive white pigment rubbed into the incised lines. Today among the Kogi, this color combination symbolizes the seminal power of solar-related males within the dualistic Tairona universe.

115. BEAD

Calima, upper Cauca River Valley, Colombia
Yotoco Period, 500–800 CE (?)
Emerald
4.8 × 3.5 × 3.2 cm
2009.20.9

Exotic commodities were coveted throughout ancient Colombia by those enjoying elevated social and political status. Rare items, made so by their scarcity, their having come from a long distance, or unusual physical properties such as color or transparency, signified the owner's control over resources and people. Some commodities also exemplified mythical or spiritual properties and thus were particularly potent possessions to be displayed as emblems of status and power.

Emeralds come from the Eastern Cordillera of the Andes Mountains, which dominate western Colombia, the region divided south-to-north by the impressive Magdalena River. Emeralds' scarcity, rich and transparent green color, and symbolic association with fertility transformed the stone into a potent object of prestige and authority. Beads made from lightly worked emeralds, many of considerable size, adorned the bodies of important individuals throughout Colombia and were coveted among other societies in Panama and Costa Rica, a few even finding their way as far north as Mesoamerica.

116–19. FOOTED DISHES WITH ANIMAL MOTIFS

Nariño (Tuza), southern Colombia or northern Ecuador
Late Period, 900–1500 CE
Earthenware, slip paint
No. 116 (TL.2009.20.277): height 9.4 cm, diameter 19.6 cm
No. 117 (TL.2009.20.278): height 9.5 cm, diameter 18.8 cm
No. 118 (TL.2009.20.279): height 7.9 cm, diameter 20.8 cm
No. 119 (TL.2009.20.280): height 9.2 cm, diameter 18.5 cm

Dishes with annular supports are found throughout the Nariño-Carchí region, which straddles the international border between Colombia and Ecuador, although stylistic differences distinguish highly localized sub-traditions.[1] The Tuza complex, found at archaeological sites in the upper Guaitara River region and perhaps related to the historical Pastos people of the area, is differentiated by the use of positive painting rather than negative-resist painting found elsewhere in the region. Further, Tuza decorative motifs are almost exclusively restricted to the vessel interior. The designs are arranged in bands with negative space or a single motif at the center of the bowl (no. 119), or the design is segmented into discrete areas divided by framing lines (no. 117).

These four bowls feature zoomorphic and geometric motifs. The decorative format of no. 116 combines embellished triangles variously arranged to create vertical and spiral forms. On the other three bowls animal representations feature four deer, including a buck and three does or antler-less young bucks (no. 117), a bird with outstretched wings (no. 118), and a ring of feline-headed figures holding staff-like objects (no. 119). This latter bowl's program features thin, delicately rendered figural forms that move elegantly around the vessel's circular pictorial field. The painter took into account the image-altering curvature of the bowl, elongating the figures' legs so that their body proportions do not appear distorted by the concave arc of the vessel.

Note

1. Santa Ana 1986, 14–15.

116

117

118

119

120. FEMALE FIGURINE

Valdivia, Ecuador
2700–1400 BCE
Earthenware, slip paint
5.9 × 2.7 × 1.3 cm
TL.2009.20.230

Among the earliest ceramic figural art in South America is the figurine tradition of the Valdivia culture, which arose on the Guayas Coast of southwestern Ecuador sometime after 3200 BCE. The tiny figurines' highly stylized form attests to the Valdivia artists' sculptural sensitivity and the expressive possibilities of the understated form. Valdivia figurines are made of two rolls of clay pressed together and sculpted to form the standing figure. This lady's elaborate hair style, with its typically bulbous shape, remained popular for millennia among native peoples of western Ecuador.

Most Valdivia figurines portray nude females, prompting their interpretation as fertility objects. However, they usually are encountered in domestic contexts and frequently found intentionally broken. It is more likely that they played a role in rituals concerned with daily life and survival, especially childbirth and healing ceremonies, an interpretation based on modern practices among traditional healers throughout western South America.

The Chorrera art style developed from the Valdivia tradition and spread throughout the southern coastal and adjacent inland regions. This was a time of social, political, economic, and artistic innovations prompted by agricultural improvements and a growing population.[1] New settlements and towns, with ever-larger numbers of inhabitants, triggered the need for methods to manage village life and ensure the well-being of the community, which, in turn, led to greater social hierarchy. Hand-in-hand with the growing social complexity was the appearance of more complex religious practices. Both developments encouraged the desire for novel artworks to express the new sociopolitical and spiritual ideologies that characterize this dynamic time throughout ancient Ecuador.

At this time, the earlier Valdivia figurine tradition developed into an elaborate figural art form with such novel artistic expressions

as the elegant, mold-made sculptures of the Jama Coaque and La Tolita styles of Ecuador's northwestern coastal region.[2] This example (no. 122) likely pertains to the La Tolita style, which is differentiated by its heightened naturalism. Elsewhere in Ecuador, artists manipulated the human figure to serve as the primary form for vessels. The Chorrera-style bowl (no. 121) features a prone human body as its upper section lying atop the vessel's platformlike base. The artist accentuated the plain body by applying red slip paint to the head, feet, inside rim of the vessel opening, and its base. The figure wears ear spools, and the closed eyes and slightly open lips suggest a ritual pose.

Technical Commentary

No. 121: The combination of building techniques used in the construction of this Chorrera anthropomorphic vessel can be

121. EFFIGY BOWL

Chorrera, Ecuador
1200–300 BCE
Earthenware, burnished slip paint
10.2 × 16 × 10.2 cm
TL.2009.20.117

122. HEAD

Tumaco-La Tolita, Ecuador
300 BCE–600 CE
Earthenware, emerald
17.8 × 12.7 × 9.4 cm
TL.2009.20.182

121

122

Fig. 1. Detail of the face showing applied facial features

seen in the hand modeling of the face and arms as opposed to the regularity of the raft and body of the figure resulting from the use of a mold. The impressions and working marks on the interior of the vessel indicate that the raft and the body may have been built in separate molds and then joined. The arms were added to the molded vessel. Features such as lips, ears, eyelids, and nose are also formed from added pieces of clay (fig. 1). Shallow striations covering the surface of the figure's body appear to be the result of the building and smoothing process.

The bowl is made from light buff-colored clay, which is still visible on the body of the figure and the interior of the vessel. Dark red slip, burnished to a light sheen, has been used on the figure's hair and feet, the raft, and the inner edge of the rim. Dark discolorations present on the surface of the exposed ceramic are a result of the firing process (BF).

Notes

1. Felleman 1982, 7–13.

2. Ithaca 1982, 47 (J. Scott).

123. SNUFF TRAY

Jama Coaque, Ecuador

300 BCE–600 CE

Earthenware

15.6 × 11.4 × 18.8 cm

TL.2009.20.126

As an outgrowth of the earlier Chorrera ceramic sculptural tradition, Jama-Coaque pottery focuses on the human figure and the portrayal of ritual life.[1] Most Jama-Coaque ceramic figures were formed from molds, and hand modeling completed the piece. Here, however, no evidence of mold construction is discernible, the lively figure and its attached tray being modeled entirely by hand. In addition, the figure's animated and threatening pose diverges from the majority of Jama-Coaque ceramic figures, which typically are more static in body position and attitude.

The figure portrays a spirit being or perhaps a shaman in spirit form ready to battle supernatural forces. The being's teeth and clawed paws recall those of the jaguar, here with an especially shaggy fur. The jagged tongue and rectangles hanging from the ear ornaments may refer to the being's supernatural powers. Shamanic transformation was aided by the ingestion of psychoactive plants ground into a fine powder and ingested as a snuff, which was served on trays such as this figural example.

Note

1. Ithaca 1982, 48 (J. Scott)

PERU & BOLIVIA

The dramatic landscape of western South America has always challenged indigenous Andean peoples, who have responded in ingenious ways to survive in the region's highly diverse and often exigent micro-environments. The magnificent landscapes were the inspiration for unique social systems and religious ideologies that were the foundation of this great civilization. Harnessing the demanding environments—including the world's driest coastal desert, desolate and cold highlands, and formidable mountains nearly impossible to traverse—Andean peoples excelled in agriculture, marine fishing, and animal husbandry to nourish and sustain the many cultures stretching from Ecuador to Chile. Their success fostered the development of distinct artistic traditions, including the discovery of metallurgy and one of the world's most complex and aesthetically impressive traditions in the fiber arts.

A seminal feature of Andean civilization is the early development of interaction among peoples living in discrete eco-zones, which molded the distinctive sociopolitical system shared by all Andean peoples. Those living in one zone devised novel ways to exploit the local resources and then traded the products from their region to neighboring groups living in other eco-zones. For example, highland peoples utilized upland pasturelands to herd camelids (especially llamas) and to grow quinoa and potatoes. Those living at lower montane altitudes grew maize, vegetables, and fruits, while peoples inhabiting dry coastal areas developed extensive irrigation systems to water warmer-climate crops while procuring a wide variety of marine resources from the rich Pacific Ocean. The cross-zone exchange network was firmly established by 3000 BCE, its sociopolitical outcome being the creation of interconnected groups of different people aligned

by need and later by social, political, and religious traditions. This network culminated in the famous Andean paved roads that were expanded by the Inkas (1400–1532 CE) into a 10,000+ mile-long system to efficiently move goods and information throughout the Inka empire from Ecuador to central Chile. An interconnected system of way stations supported by the state and manned by a professional class of runners linked the Inka capital, Cuzco, with the farthest reaches of the empire in five days or less.

Andean cosmology is based on the need to maintain cosmic balance. The Andean system holds that paired opposites were the building blocks of the cosmos, and such dyads as gender (male-female), environment (hot-cold, wet-dry), and time (day-night) were in constant motion. The cosmos was viewed as animate, and thus nature was enlivened by paired, interactive forces. *Pacha Mama* (mother earth) was of particular importance, and Andean peoples frequently made reverential offerings to ensure her fecundity. The landscape also preserved distant history from pre-human times, with certain features believed to be the sacred locales and ruins of these ancient beings. In essence, Andean peoples inhabited a living cosmos in which past and present constantly interacted and in which dyads were central to the vital universe. This ideology permeated all things, including artistic media. Gold and silver, for example, were paired opposites symbolic of the male-female dyad. Of particular importance in the Andean belief system is the principle of life and death being but a continuum between two opposites of the same force. Death is not a final void but simply another form of being infused with the same vital essence that animates the world of the living. This seminal precept prompted the production of extraordinary objects as tomb offerings for use in the other, post-death life.

The origin of Andean civilization reaches back before 3400 BCE. By this time large settlements with public architecture were commonplace, and artisans produced portable works in stone, pottery, and natural fibers (especially camelid wools and cotton). The ensuing thousand years witnessed the establishment of local artistic traditions in a variety of media, including precious metals, that would be at the heart of the civilization for the next two and a half millennia. The emerging ruling class drew authority from special relationships with the sacred, animate powers of the universe, and they were responsible for maintaining universal balance for society as a whole. The ruling class sponsored monumental architecture and finely crafted ceramics, precious metalwork, and expertly woven textiles whose imagery and quality underscored personal prestige, social and political power, and religious beliefs.

From 500 BCE to 1400 CE, regional states flowered throughout Peru and northern Bolivia. The Moche and Nasca peoples governed Peru's north and south coasts respectively, while other groups in the highlands also developed into sizable polities. A major ideological and sociopolitical shift occurred during the Middle Horizon (600–900 CE) with the rise of the Wari (Huari) of Peru's southern highlands and the Tiwanaku society of northern Bolivia. They introduced a revised religious ideology and embarked on the building of two empires that spread north into Ecuador (by the Wari) and south to Chile (by the Tiwanaku). Drought conditions perhaps hastened the demise of the Wari/Tiwanaku phenomenon, with frequent dry periods wreaking havoc on agricultural production, especially during the latter part of

the Middle Horizon and challenging the sociopolitical *status quo*. After the breakup of these two imperial powerhouses, regional states once again held sway during the subsequent Late Intermediate Period (900–1400 CE). The Sicán (Lambayeque) and Chimú peoples directed affairs along the North Coast, whereas the Chancay confederation of the Central Coast and the Ica of the South Coast were the major players in their respective regions.

The Late Horizon (1400–1532 CE) is the time of the Inka empire, which at its height controlled the largest territory of any political entity in the world. Arising in the southern highlands during the early 1400s, the Inkas blended previously independent societies into their socio-political and economic systems, imposing uniformity in most aspects of life, from food production and distribution to clothing style and decoration, religious ideology, and all manner of artistic form and expression. Such standardization provided an effective means of management and control of the far-flung and multiethnic empire. Surprisingly, although the Inka state imposed uniformity on most forms of art and architecture, their creations avoided the typical drop in quality associated with such rigidity. Instead, Inka art and architecture are among the most unique and recognizable styles in the ancient Americas, with regional interpretations that enliven the corporate form. Monolithic yet intricate and delicate, Inka art absorbed and reinterpreted the shared geometricism of the pan-Andean aesthetic, transforming it into a new and innovative narrative tradition.[1]

The sixteenth-century Spanish invasion nearly obliterated all Andean artistic traditions. The conquest certainly triggered the destruction of thousands of artworks, especially those made of precious metals, which were melted into ingots and sent to Europe to fill the royal coffers and adorn Catholic churches. At the same time, Spanish ecclesiastics and other entrepreneurs took control of local textile production and imposed on Andean weavers Euro-Christian icons and decorative schemes. As in pre-Spanish times, the textile artists produced magnificent fabrics for their new masters of church and state. The importance of textiles to Andean cultural identity and daily life is highlighted by their present survival as a vibrant indigenous art form, its weavers continuing to create exceptionally fine textiles in wool, cotton, and synthetic yarns.[2]

Notes

1. Stone-Miller 2002a, 184.

2. Boston 1992, 35–36.

124. MANIOC EFFIGY BOTTLE

Tembladera, North Coast, Peru
Late Initial Period to Early Horizon, 600–200 BCE
Burnished earthenware
27.5 × 14.7 × 22.9 cm
TL.2009.20.101

125. CHIRIMOYA (?) EFFIGY BOTTLE

Cupisnique, North Coast, Peru
Late Initial Period to Early Horizon, 600–200 BCE
Earthenware, incising
Height 21.4 cm, diameter 14.7 cm
TL.2009.20.158

Peru's northern coast was home to many early societies that developed individualistic expressions within the broader Chavín style of the Early Horizon. Tembladera ceramics (no. 124) feature tall, slender, and slightly out-flaring spouts, whereas Cupisnique vessels are visually more substantial and have wider and shorter spouts, often with thickened rims (no. 125). Cupisnique vessels frequently contrast a matte-finish or scored surface with a smoothed one to embellish the fruit, vegetable, or animal represented, although abstraction of the natural form is typical of Cupisnique artistry. This stirrup-spout bottle may depict the chirimoya fruit, although it also shares features with the *Spondylus* shell (spiny oyster), a valued ritual material whose inner red surface made it a highly valued commodity for adornments among peoples from northern Mexico to Chile.

The Tembladera-style vessel (no. 124) is modeled in the shape of the manioc, an important lowland tuber that was a primary source of starch throughout the ancient Americas, from the Caribbean to northern South America. The art style is typified by large, curvilinear areas that are well-smoothed and slipped dark brown or black. The focus is the sculptural form rather than the surface decoration. Manioc is among the important foods from warmer coastal environs traded to highland peoples such as those at Chavín de Huantar, the primary political and ritual Chavín center in the adjacent highlands. The sociopolitical unification that ensued from these early exchange contacts established the interactive networks along which social, political, and religious concepts spread. These complex relationships are reflected in the similar artistic forms and architectural features found throughout northern and central Peru at this early time.

124

125

126. GOURD

Moche, North Coast, Peru

Early Intermediate Period, 100–650 CE

Gourd, shell, and green stone inlays

7 × 11.7 × 10.4 cm

TL.2009.20.272

Moche artworks are often decorated with narrative imagery conveying myths or historical reenactments thereof. Others depict important members of Moche society, from rulers to warriors to religious specialists.[1] The images follow a symbolic system that, like a language, has its own vocabulary and grammar. To understand the narrative, one must be literate in the symbolic system. In the case of Moche art, some narratives have been deciphered by combining archaeological data, narrative analysis, and ethnohistorical information.[2] In other instances, such as the scene adorning this gourd vessel, the full meaning of the imagery remains enigmatic.

The gourd's imagery, created by inlays of shell and stone, may be associated with the broader theme of ritual hunts, which among the Moche had shamanic overtones.[3] This interpretation is based on features of the main figure, the presence of the cavorting dog, and the smaller-sized human assistant, all common elements of Moche hunting scenes.[4] The figure's hands (one is missing) are carved from *Spondylus* shell and protrude from the gourd; a small perforation through the palm indicates that he originally held something—perhaps a hunter's spear thrower. Ritual hunts often seek sea lions, deer, or foxes, although birds may also be the selected prey as implied in this scene.[5] The presence of fishlike and circular motifs floating in the picture plane suggests a coastal location for the event.[6] The small step-

fret motifs on the ground line (one of white shell and one of turquoise inlay) imply that the event is taking place in sight of architecture (i.e., a town locale) rather than in the wilds. The large, frontal figure's identity remains problematic because he lacks a headdress, which, in Moche art, provides important identifying features. It is likely that the headdress was found on the vessel's lid, which has not survived.

Although the meaning of this gourd's scene is not fully understood, the tiny vessel is a fine example of delicate inlay artistry and expressive narrative rivaling the painted pictorial ceramics for which the Moche are renowned. The artist follows the Andean tradition of paired opposites, here contrasting the dry, brown surface of the gourd with the reflective (waterlike) rich colors of the shell and stone inlays.

Notes

1. Los Angeles 1976, 158–73.

2. Ibid., 8–10.

3. Ibid., 178.

4. Ibid., 179–83.

5. Donnan and McClelland 1999, 120–22, 239–43.

6. Ibid., 179.

127. WARRIOR EFFIGY BOTTLE

Moche, North Coast, Peru

Early Intermediate Period,
Phases III–IV, 300–600 CE

Burnished earthenware, shell inlay

21.9 × 13.9 × 16.4 cm

TL.2009.20.156

Warfare was a common tool for political advancement in the ancient Andes, although it often had ritual connotations and goals. The so-called Warrior Narrative or Sacrifice Ceremony, one of the most common scenes adorning Moche painted pottery, features ritual combat among finely dressed members of the ruling class. The narrative is composed of a sequence of acts, including the warriors' preparation for battle, the combat and capture of the vanquished, the removal of the captives' finery, their ritual bleeding, and their presentation by the victorious warrior to a main figure.[1] The blood of the elite was an especially efficacious religious offering, often poured on the earth to ensure the fertility of mother earth and maintain nature's balance.

This expressive libation vessel is molded in the form of a warrior, identified by the combat club grasped in his left hand and the small round shield held aloft to protect his head. The elaborate tunic is that of a member of the *kuraka* elite of Moche society, here decorated with shell inlays. Such finery implies a warrior rendered in ceremonial attire rather than a battlefield figure.[2]

Of special note is his seated position, which does not match any of the stances taken by warriors in the Warrior Narrative/Sacrifice Ceremony. Instead, the monkey head (perhaps a head mask?) and fully human body suggest the portrayal of a shaman-warrior ready to do battle with supernatural forces. Monkeys are commonly employed by Andean artists to symbolize shamanic powers, and the simian would thus be a fitting form to convey a warrior's special prowess.[3] Figural bottles depicting warriors, other members of the nobility, and supernatural beings are common offerings found in high-status Moche burials; a shaman-warrior would be an important protector to accompany a member of the elite into the next life.

Notes

1. Donnan and McClelland 1999, 69. See also Alva and Donnan 1993, 127–41.

2. Los Angeles 1976, 179.

3. Stone-Miller 2002a, 15.

128. EFFIGY BOTTLE

Recuay, Northern Highlands, Peru
Early Intermediate Period, 200 BCE–500 CE
Earthenware, slip paint
Height 28.3 cm, diameter 20.6 cm
2009.20.37

Northern Peru's pottery traditions focus on three-dimensionality, the vessels often modeled into a variety of volumetric forms depicting human figures, fruits, or vegetables and even architecture. The coastal Moche and their highland Recuay neighbors were masters of the modeled form, having explored and perfected this tradition whose origins reach back as much as a thousand years among cultures of the Early Horizon (900–200 BCE). Recuay pottery is typically thin-walled and made from a kaolin-based clay. Vessels are decorated with negative-resist and positive slip painting as well as an unusual post-fire, resist black organic pigment. The varied resist-painting techniques allowed Recuay artists to create complex design fields on the positive, slip-painted backgrounds.

Recuay art, and especially its narrative pottery, features the Andean concepts of dualism and reciprocity as key universal facets. Emphasis was placed on dyads such as male-female, which is aptly expressed by this extraordinary figural bottle. A finely dressed noble woman stands at opposing sides of the four-sided vessel, while a male personage flanks the other two faces. The males pertain to a second dyad of warrior and captive, the latter represented as a trophy head rather than a full figure. The women and warrior cradle *qero*-like ceremonial cups in their hands; the male figure also clutches a war club in his right hand. His fine clothing and headdress identify him as a member of the ruling class. The iconic face in his headdress recalls depictions of ancestors and cult figures as prime shamanic beings that often adorn the heads of authority figures from earliest times throughout Peru.

Considered together, this four-sided figural vessel embodies the Andean ideology of war and sacrifice to ensure the earth's fertility and maintain universal balance. The taking of captives for ritual sacrifice was facilitated by the victor's shamanic power, here implied by the male figure's headdress. As elsewhere in ancient Peru, this ceremonial pageant was a sacred necessity and the responsibility of the nobility.[1] It is reflected in stone sculptures from the Recuay area (the highland Callejón de Huaylas region), which feature small trophy heads and larger male figures carrying clubs, shields, or decapitated heads. The Recuay tradition of public stone sculptures portraying women echoes their depictions on pottery vessels, signaling the importance of female participants in both ritual and political events.

Note

1. Stone-Miller 2002a, 94–95.

129

129. LOBSTER EFFIGY VESSEL

Nasca, South Coast, Peru

Early Intermediate Period,

Phases III–IV, 300–600 CE

Earthenware, burnished slip paint

13.5 × 24.1 × 10.4 cm

2009.20.55

130. DISH WITH BEAN IMAGERY

Nasca, South Coast, Peru

Early Intermediate Period,

Phases II–III, 200–300 CE

Earthenware, burnished slip paint

Height 4.5 cm, diameter 9.7 cm

TL.2009.20.110

The coast of Peru is bathed in the Humboldt Current, which sweeps cold water from the Antarctic along the South American coast and northwards to Mexico and the Pacific Northwest. Rich in plankton and other marine animals, the Humboldt Current supports one of the world's most fertile fishing grounds. Early Andean peoples harvested its bounty, with fish and shellfish being a primary source of protein not only for coastal peoples but also those in the highlands. This lobster effigy vessel (no. 129), with its small bridge-spout handle typical of Nasca ceramics, is a masterful example of the ceramic effigy vessel form.

Nasca pottery is famous for its elegantly proportioned vessels with very thin walls. Surfaces are hard, very shiny, and typically survive for thousands of years in pristine condition. Nasca ceramics are painted with elaborate designs, symbolic motifs, or pictorial narratives, and their wide variety of hues surpasses all Andean ceramic traditions. The aesthetic focus is on precisely drafted outlines and color fields, which lend clarity and gracefulness to the otherwise simple pattern of beans that decorates this small dish (no. 130).

While the Humboldt Current brings marine riches to the Peruvian coast, it also produces one of the world's driest deserts.

To survive in such an inhospitable environment, coastal peoples constructed extensive and elaborate irrigation systems to channel waters from the highlands to the rich but arid soils of the coast. The Nasca are renowned for their underground systems of canals that reduced the loss of water from surface evaporation. Thus the region was able to grow prodigious amounts of food, especially beans, maize, squash and a variety of fruits, all of which were valuable commodities throughout the Andes.

130

Fig. 1. Detail of side, showing shell inlay and twisted band at forehead

131. FEMALE EFFIGY FIGURE

Nasca, South Coast, Peru

Early Intermediate Period, 200 BCE–500 CE

Sperm whale tooth, shell, hair

7.6 × 2.7 × 2.4 cm

2009.20.7

Andean civilization is renowned for spectacular textiles that were at the heart of social politics and economics from earliest times. The fiber arts permeated all facets of daily existence, from clothing to protect the body to bridges spanning treacherous gorges. The form, materials, quality, and decorative imagery on clothing conveyed a person's social status or political affiliation and even recounted his or her specific accomplishments on behalf of the state. This female figure originally was dressed in clothing appropriate to her meaning as an offering—perhaps a building dedication cache or ritual deposit at a *huaca*, a sacred location where divine forces are concentrated.

Coastal Andean peoples were keen observers of the vast ocean world. The Nasca, in particular, relied heavily on marine resources for food and materials for a variety of uses, such as the whale tooth from which this captivating lady was carved. The salty ocean and its unusual creatures constituted a dyadic opposition to the earth with its fresh waters. The carving of a ritual figurine from the tooth of a gigantic marine creature certainly carried extra spiritual significance.

Technical Commentary

This small figurine is carved from sperm whale tooth.[1] Incised lines indicate her sex, while small drilled holes at her sides open up negative space between the shoulders and hands, which are attached at the hips. Only her nose is carved in relief; the figure's lips are rendered with a thin incised line filled with red pigment. Central black pupils are offset by triangular shell fragments adhered with resin. The rectangular shape of the head is reinforced by a section of purple shell at its back. Sections of this same purple shell are inlaid in front of both ears (fig. 1). The head is covered with hair (human?) bound with a twisted vegetal fiber covered in a dark-colored resin (JL).

Note

1. References for the use of sperm whale tooth and killer whale tooth to create similar figurines can be found on the website of the Foundation for the Advancement of Mesoamerican Studies. (FAMSI) (www.famsi.org). Under close examination this "ivory" material lacked the distinctive patterning of either elephant or walrus ivory. The inner dentine layer on this figure is darker than the outer layer (see the lower legs, which represent the interior of the tooth). This evidence, in addition to the size of the figure and the noted use of sperm whale tooth by the Nazca, helps to confirm the sperm whale tooth identification.

132. LIBATION VESSEL (QERO)

Nasca, South Coast, Peru
Early Intermediate Period, 550–650 CE
Earthenware, burnished slip paint
Height 20 cm, diameter at rim 10.7 cm
TL.2009.20.90

133. LIBATION VESSEL (QERO)

Tiwanaku-Moquegua,
Southern Highlands, Peru
Middle Horizon, 500–800 CE
Earthenware, burnished slip paint
Height 11.4, diameter 10.2 cm
TL.2009.20.91

Nasca pottery artists excelled in painting dynamic imagery using a wide variety of slip-paint colors. They preferred relatively unencumbered vessel surfaces, so that the paintings flow across the ceramic object. Many images are those of deities or iconic references to religious ideology. In other instances, it is clear that the reference is cloth, a highly valued commodity throughout the Andean world, as is seen on these two drinking vessels. The energetic geometric patterns on the tall Nasca vessel (no. 132), which dates to the end of the Early Intermediate Period (ca. 550–650 CE), have their counterparts in textiles that have survived in the dry southern coastal deserts as well as in painted renderings of clothed figures depicted on pottery. Nasca textile artists were masters of a variety of weaving techniques, including brocade, tapestry, and the difficult and time-consuming discontinuous warp-and-weft method.

The design on the smaller *qero* (no. 133) recalls the extreme abstraction that typifies Wari-style textiles from the southern coast. The step-fret/curl is a frequent Wari decorative motif, perhaps alluding to an undulating ground line/architectural feature like that seen at the base of the carved narrative on the Gate of the Sun at Tiwanaku.[1] However, Wari textile imagery was purposefully manipulated to the point of unrecognizability of the original form, such intentionally designed camouflage making problematic any interpretation of the motif decorating this beaker. Such obfuscation served to highlight the artistry of the weaver, who exercised great skill to maintain the original essence of such a completely abstracted representation.[2]

Notes

1. Conklin 2004, 180–81.

2. Boston 1992, 35–36.

132

133

134. CANTEEN-SHAPED BOTTLE

Nasca-Wari, South Coast, Peru

Middle Horizon, 600–800 CE

Earthenware, burnished slip paint

17.8 × 14.5 × 9.2 cm

TL.2009.20.105

Following a period of ruinous droughts caused by changes in the Humboldt Current beginning before 600 CE, major sociopolitical changes occurred throughout Peru and northern Bolivia. New centers arose in the highlands that were better adapted to deal with significant environmental changes than were the Moche and Nasca coastal societies. The newly dominant states, Tiwanaku (Tiahuanco) in northern Bolivia and Wari (Huari) in Peru's southern highlands, reoriented the Andean political and ideological terrain. Novel interpretations of pan-Andean social and religious ideals were now expressed by new aesthetics and iconographic configurations that reinvigorated the artistic landscape. Tiwanaku and especially Wari art styles share a preference for iconic obfuscation achieved by geometric abstraction, yet the artists followed established templates to ensure comprehension of the underlying narrative.

The primary Wari/Tiwanaku iconographic program features the frontal depiction of what has been interpreted as a principal deity (the so-called Frontal Staff Figure) holding a staff in each hand and flanked by winged attendants. The most famous rendering of this being is carved on the front of the massive Gate of the Sun at Tiwanaku, Bolivia.[1] On this ceramic bottle, the artist chose to eliminate the body and render only the supernatural being's head although she/he included the typical condor-headed "tears" and rays emanating from the head. The rays likely refer to the spiritual power of the being, implied here by condor heads and tail feathers but elsewhere, such as on Tiwanaku's Gate of the Sun, by puma heads.[2] The ritualistic nature of this vessel's imagery is reinforced by its modeled form, which makes reference to a stylized *Spondylus* shell. This valuable commodity, found primarily in deep waters off the Ecuadorian and Peruvian coasts, indicated high status and pertained to spiritual themes of sacrifice and spirit transformation throughout the ancient Andes.[3]

Notes

1. Denver 2004, 36.

2. Stone-Miller 2002a, 132–34.

3. Stone-Miller 2002b, 40–41, 95–96.

135. TROPHY-HEAD EFFIGY VESSEL

Wari, possibly Ayacucho Basin,
Southern Highlands, Peru
Middle Horizon, 500–800 CE
Earthenware, burnished slip paint
10.8 × 12.7 × 12.7 cm
TL.2009.20.97

The taking of trophy heads was an important politico-religious act among the Tiwanaku and Wari peoples, whose emergence as dominant societies defines the Middle Horizon. Trophy heads frequently adorn the walls of public buildings at Tiwanaku, and they often take the form of drinking vessels, as in this example. Among the later

Inkas, it was common practice to transform a captured enemy warrior's skull into a libation vessel. When used during ceremonies of victory and other politically charged events, the display of such items highlighted the might of the user and implied his appropriation of the vanquished warrior's powers. The preponderance of trophy-head drinking cups among the Tiwanaku and Wari suggests a similar belief among these two cultures, which were ancestral to the Late Horizon Inkas.[1]

The act of trophy head-taking extends far beyond the brutality of warfare and pursuit of political domination. In ancient Peru, ritual decapitation was likened to harvesting

fruits and vegetables, and the blood spilling from the body was believed to fertilize mother earth (Pacha Mama). Thus the vanquished warrior served as a magical force that revitalized the earth and maintained the balance of nature. In essence, the warrior never died but instead lived on as a vital, animate member of the victorious community, which had absorbed his powers for universal good.[2]

Notes

1. Kolata 2004, 107.

2. Ibid., 111–12.

136. VESSEL

Chancay, Central Coast, Peru

Late Intermediate Period, 1000–1470 CE

Earthenware, slip paint

Height 29.7 cm, diameter 12.2 cm

2009.20.35

The Chancay art style dominated Peru's Central Coast during the Late Intermediate Period, although there was no centralized, overarching state authority ruling the region. Textiles and pottery were the primary artistic media, the former being among the most colorful, visually complex, and technically excellent weavings ever produced in Peru. Chancay pottery, on the other hand, is often rather casually or carelessly painted, its slip characterized by a matte surface finish and a palette restricted to white and black (with the infrequent addition of red or beige). The low-fired Chancay ceramics make them susceptible to surface damage, unlike the earlier pottery of the Moche, Nasca, and Wari cultures. On the other hand, Chancay painting can be as lively as that of any Andean tradition. The acute difference in quality between Chancay ceramics and textiles reflects sociopolitical divisions in Chancay culture. Burial patterns indicate that the painted ceramics were consumed by all levels of Chancay society, whereas fine textiles and precious metal objects were restricted to members of higher status. As elsewhere in the Andean world, artistic quality and materials conveyed messages of hierarchy and power.

This tall, narrow vessel features the frontal rendering of a male figure. He grasps a puma-headed staff in each hand, and two serpent-headed rays emanate from his head. These pan-Andean features link the figure to traditional depictions of supernatural beings or deities and shamans. The bird painted at the top of the vessel reflects this theme in its crescent-shaped head adornment, which distinguishes the "Sicán Deity" or "Sicán Lord," who may be a culture hero or a deity among cultures to the north. The "Sicán Lord" is associated primarily with the Sicán and later Chimú societies of the North Coast, although the Chimú extended their influence over the Chancay people at the end of the Late Intermediate Period.[1] It is not improbable that this symbol of divinity and/or sacred ancestry was adopted by the Chancay. The painter of this tall vessel animated the scene by filling the background with black avian footprints, which, at the least, lend motion to the bird if not implying its ritual performance.

Note

1. Stone-Miller 2002a, 158.

137. LLAMA EFFIGY

Chancay, Central Coast, Peru
Late Intermediate Period, 1000–1470 CE
Earthenware, slip paint
21.1 × 40.4 × 16 cm
2009.20.49

The llama, a native camelid of the Americas, touched all aspects of Andean life. The llama—the only native American beast of burden—was used primarily to transport goods from the coastal deserts to the highest mountain plains. Well adapted to the extremes of the Andean environment, including climate, terrain, and altitude, the llama was at the heart of every Andean home. The llama and its camelid cousins (alpaca, guanaco, and vicuña) provided the all-important hairs that were spun into fibers to weave warm garments of considerable strength and durability. Such clothing was crucial for survival during cold Andean nights and in the *altiplano* highlands. Llamas also provided body heat for shepherds and other laborers who could not return to a warm home every night. Llama blood was an important ritual offering, and its meat was occasionally consumed for protein, although the high value of the living animal made these latter uses infrequent and of special significance.

During the Late Intermediate Period, the Chancay Valley and adjacent Chillón Drainage developed an energetic corporate style of architecture and art. Large amounts of ceramics were produced and distributed among the ruling elite as well as those of lesser status. Among these are the distinctive mold-made and hand-modeled sculptures of humans (both men and women) and animals. This engaging sculpture of a young llama captures the animal's natural inquisitiveness. It cocks its head slightly to the side as if watching intently some unseen activity. The artist divided the llama's face into two halves, painting one side white and the other black, following the Andean principle of duality and balance. The artist also designated the animal's sex as male, and embellished the body with black spots, one of the natural coloration schemes of the animal. Typical of the distinctive Chancay pottery style is the somewhat haphazard modeling and painting, which enhance the piece's charm.

138. HEAD EFFIGY BEAD

Moche, North Coast, Peru

Early Intermediate Period, 400–600 CE

Silvered copper sheet, *Spondylus* shell, malachite

6.5 × 7.7 × 3.7 cm

TL.2009.20.261

The Moche developed the first state-level political system in the ancient Andes during the Early Intermediate Period (200 BCE–500 CE) in response to wide-ranging events throughout the northern coast. The region's growing populations and occasional droughts of years' duration heightened competition for arable land and precious water. A new elite class, the *kuraka*, arose to meet the challenges of effective survival by exerting control over coastal resources, from land and water allocations to the human labor needed for such crucial construction projects as large-scale irrigation systems and monumental architecture conveying socio-political and spiritual power. The *kuraka* also controlled the all-important local and long-distance exchange networks that ensured the availability of both basic commodities and luxury goods.

The authority of the *kuraka* was based on an ideology that claimed their descent from mythic founders. Thus, although the gods were the ultimate source of power, mythical human figures became principal kingpins in the Moche politico-religious schematic. The five major river valleys of the northern coast were united, to varying degrees, under the commanding *kuraka* socio-political framework. They not only administered all manner of subsistence, social, and religious affairs, but also sponsored the production of prodigious amounts of artworks that denoted high status and underscored the ideological basis of socio-political hierarchy.[1]

Members of the *kuraka* were adorned with finely crafted jewelry made of silver and gold and often embellished with precious shell and stone inlays. Noblemen buried in the royal tombs of Sipán, an important Moche center, were festooned in all manner of precious metal adornments whose imagery indicated their political office and specified their ceremonial roles during enactments of the Sacrifice Ceremony, which frequently was represented on Moche pottery.[2] This large silver bead may be the head of the so-called Decapitator, a key supernatural being associated with human sacrifice

and warrior power. The lord buried in Sipán Tomb 1 was dressed as the Warrior Priest of the Sacrifice Ceremony. He was adorned with jewelry depicting this fearsome being, which thereby connected him to ritual warfare and decapitation sacrifice. Similar gold, copper, and silver effigy bead necklaces bedecked the individuals in Tombs 2 and 3, some beads having the fanged teeth of the deity, whereas others feature humanlike teeth. In this example, the hair, face, and large earflares recall human portrayals, whereas the shape of the mouth, which likely makes reference to the snarl of a feline predator, is more typical of

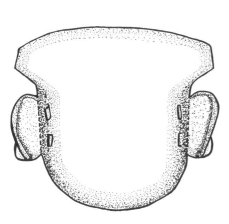

Fig. 1. Illustration of reverse showing tabs used to secure sheet metal ears

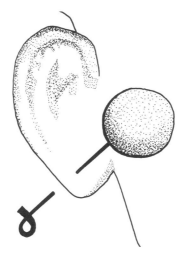

Fig. 2. Illustration showing attachment of *Spondylus* shell with post and twisted fastener

Fig. 3. Overall top view of head showing detail of hair

the Decapitator supernatural being. As such, this large silver bead may have alluded to the wearer's spiritual power.

Technical Commentary

This hollow-back open form was created exclusively from sheet metal typical of Moche metalwork from Sipán.[3] Separately made ears and ear spools were attached with slots and tabs fastened by bending and twisting the metal (figs. 1, 2).[4] Given the corroded nature of the surfaces, it is difficult to say whether the face and hair were created from a single sheet or whether the hair was created separately and joined (fig. 3). When viewed from the top, the hair is interestingly rendered in opposing directions and at slightly different heights. Variation among similarly shaped beads has been cited as evidence that some were individually crafted.[5] There is also evidence for the use of rigid forms or molds for the fabrication of sheet metal figures.[6]

Both the eyes and ear spools are inlayed with nonmetallic materials; the mouth may have originally held similar inlay.[7] The eyes are made of green banded malachite inset with pupils of a white crystalline material containing flecks of blue, possibly deteriorated lapis lazuli.[8] The ear spools are set with

Spondylus shell. Analyzed areas of the ears, face, and hair all indicate metal alloys in the range of Au 10–16%, Cu 70–83%, and Ag 6–12%.[9]

The head is extremely fragile and has been repaired from several fragments; extensive copper corrosion is still in place on the reverse. The unusual texture of the lower portion of the face is a result of a previous restoration attempt to remove obscuring burial corrosion (JL).

Notes

1. Moseley 2001, 173–74.

2. Los Angeles 1993, 225–27.

3. Similar sheet metal beads and plaques can be seen in nos. 132, 163, 192, and 213—all excavated examples from Moche Royal Tombs 1, 2, and 3 at Sipán. See ibid., 123, 151, 179, 196.

4. Ibid. For similar construction of the ears from separate sheet see figs. 192, 196, p. 179, 183

5. Hörz and Kallfass 2000, 12.

6. Solid forms of metal and wood are known to have been used for Moche sheet metal work. A hollow sheet metal figure of an owl and the solid metal form over which it was shaped are illustrated in Los Angeles 1993, figs. 15, 16, 21.

7. Moche metalwork characteristically incorporated inlay of nonmetallic materials. Many examples of this are documented in Los Angeles 1993.

8. Lapis lazuli was used as inlay on similar sheet metal heads from Sipán. Ibid., 32, fig. 23.

9. Because the object appears to be silvered or gilded copper sheet metal, this analysis is not representative of the bulk alloy of the piece. The presence of both gold and silver with the copper may indicate selective color enrichment of the surfaces (compare, for example, the gold color of the ears with the overall silver appearance of the head). The use of similarly highly corroded alloys was found at Loma Negra to be Cu 87%, Ag 3% and Au 10%. Lechtman, Erlij, and Barry 1982, 9. For a discussion of the Moche's use of ternary alloys low in both gold and silver content, see ibid., 9–10.

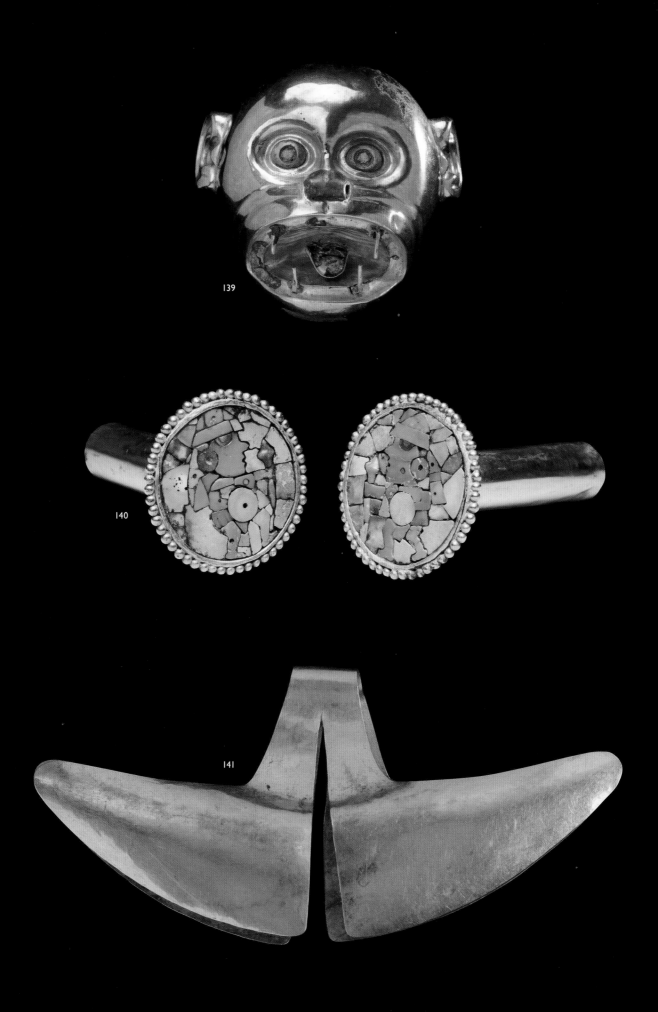

139. MONKEY EFFIGY BEAD

Moche, North Coast, Peru

Early Intermediate Period, 400–600 CE

Gold alloy, gilded copper, stone[1]

5.5 × 6.3 × 5.6 cm

Formerly New Mexico History Museum, History Collections, gift of John Bourne, 11373.45; repatriated to the Republic of Peru at the request of the Peruvian government, 2011

140. EARFLARES

Moche, North Coast, Peru

Early Intermediate Period, 400–600 CE

Gold alloy, turquoise, and stone inlay

1. Length 6.8 cm, diameter 4 cm

2. Length 6.8 cm, diameter 4.1 cm

TL.2009.20.65.1–2

141. ORNAMENT

Moche, North Coast, Peru

Early Intermediate Period, 100 BCE–600 CE

Gold alloy

6.2 × 13.4 × 2.2 cm

TL.2009.20.71

Fine craftsmanship typifies the precious metal jewelry worn by the Moche elite. From cast decorative edgings, to hammered sheets of gold rolled into shafts, to the intricate inlays of semiprecious stones, these astonishing ornaments embellished members of the elite. Not only did the dazzling artworks glitter in the brilliant desert sun, symbolically bathing the wearer in the power of the golden orb, but their symbolic imagery and exceptional artistry enhanced the status and authority of the bejeweled person.

The monkey effigy head (no. 139) displays the metalworking expertise of Moche artists and their talent for embedding delicate inlays of semiprecious stones into the metal. The imagery conveyed messages of political identity and spiritual power. This golden monkey head ornament relates to shamanic power, a connotation based on the animal's tropical forest homeland in the Amazonian hinterlands of eastern Peru far from the Moche coastal deserts. This wet and wild environment, so different from the "civilized" and arid world of the North Coast, was the source of hallucinogenic plants used by Moche shamans. An association with the untamed powers of the jungle and the supernatural world of shamans made the monkey an apt symbol of personal prowess—both worldly and spiritual.

The earflares were the personal ornaments of a member of the Moche elite. They feature a striding warrior with his club weapon thrust forward at the ready. A round shield typical of Moche combatants protects his midsection from the blows of an opponent. His conical helmet-hat is that of a high-ranking person and recalls the head covering of the Warrior Priest, the key figure in the Sacrifice Ceremony that was the culmination of Moche ritual warfare.[2]

Technical Commentary

No. 140: Each of the pair of ear flares is similarly made from both assembled sheet metal and cast elements. They are constructed from six joining metal sections and inlayed with colored stone, shell, and metal foil (fig. 1, left). A band ornamented with spheres (A) bordering the central disc is the only cast element; casting dendrites are clearly visible on the spheres; x-radiography shows that they are solid. The spheres differ slightly in size and shape and appear to have been individually made in wax. This circular border is secured behind a metal flange that is an extension of the recessed cavity for the inlaid stone (B) (fig. 1, left). A second disc (C) is connected to B by four metal tabs inserted into corresponding slots in B and C (this can be seen in the x-ray image, fig. 8 in the

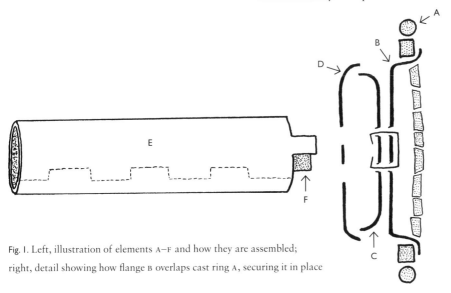

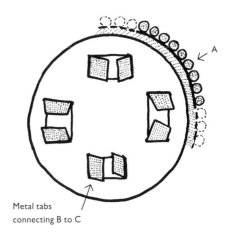

Metal tabs connecting B to C

Fig. 1. Left, illustration of elements A–F and how they are assembled; right, detail showing how flange B overlaps cast ring A, securing it in place

chapter "Approaches to Authentication").
As is typical in Andean metalwork, the tab
extensions are bent backwards on themselves
like a staple, thus securing the two elements
in place. Inverted disc D was then placed
over C. The cylinder (E) is a separate section
formed of a single sheet of metal soldered at
a seam of interlocking tabs.[3] The end of each
tube is crimped over a circular disc and the
tube itself is attached to D with metal tabs (F).

All sections, A–E, are made from a gold
alloy high in silver and particularly low in
copper (see table 1), which represents an
intentional alloy of silver and gold with an
enriched gold surface.[4] Slight differences in
the composition of sections D and E when
compared with A and B reflect corresponding
differences in surface polish and corrosion
patterns (JL).[5]

	wt%Cu	wt%Ag	wt%Au
sphere A	1.5	63.8	34.8
band (with spheres) A	0.9	65.3	33.8
flange B	1.4	56.5	42.3
disk D	2.0	49.5	48.5
post E	2.1	50.4	47.5

Table 1. Alloy composition of elements of no. 140. Compositional data are reported as average weight percent determined by x-ray fluorescence.

Notes

1. Previous work by David Scott on a very similar
object (2000, 214) identifies the use of several
alloys and gilding techniques: "The monkey is
made in a gold alloy . . . the long teeth are made
in copper that has been covered with gold by the
fusion gilding technique. The nose and eyes are
made in stones that have not been analyzed. The
monkey has been carefully made in a number of
pieces that are joined together with soldering. A
join can be seen in the head, passing across the top
of the skull." Composition of metals (wt%): outer
gold surface: Au 82%, Cu 3%, Ag 14.4%; teeth
surface: Au 61%, Cu 32%, Ag 7%; teeth substrate:
Cu 98%. D. Scott 2000, 206.

2. Los Angeles 1993, 133, fig. 143.

3. A similar use of tabs for creating an ear spool
cylinder from the Moche site of Loma Negra can
be seen in Lechtman, Erlij, and Barry 1982, 12, fig. 8.

4. Though later in date, alloys of similar high silver
and low copper were identified in technical entries
by Heather Lechtman on examples of Chimú and
Chimú-Inka metalwork. See Lechtman 1996a, 261,
262.

5. Sections A and B both have corrosion, variable
wear, and polish patterns consistent with ancient
artifacts. Sections D and E have no burial corrosion and show evidence of machine polishing.

142. BODY ADORNMENT

Malagana style, Cauca and Calima River
Valleys, Colombia
Gold
21.9 × 11.5 × 0.8 cm
Courtesy of the New Mexico History Museum,
History Collections, gift of John Bourne, 11374.45

The Calima honored dead, especially those of high social or religious status, were buried with great sanctity, their bodies adorned with sumptuous gold adornments. This type of distinctive adornment originally was thought to be a ceremonial tweezers based on the presence of similarly shaped but much smaller and unadorned gold tools. However, the rich decoration and large size argue against such an interpretation. Similar objects have been found in burials next to upper arm bones, suggesting their having been worn as arm adornments. The iconography of this piece is unusual, especially notable in the eye ridge curling into the "eyebrows."

Close examination of the piece reveals surface marks indicative of the use of modern tools. All edges show fresh cut marks and the use of a metal file to smooth the edges, a technique not in evidence on other ancient Colombian gold objects. The edges have no modulation or variation, which are typical characteristics of ancient Colombian cold-hammering techniques for producing sheets of gold.

The overall inexpert craftsmanship is anomalous for high-status Calima gold artworks. The design motifs are aggressively carved into the metal to reinforce the shallow relief decoration rather than being typically soft-hammered, embossed imagery. The surface incrustation, which resembles natural corrosion, is easily removed.

143. LIBATION VESSEL (QERO)

Chimú, North Coast, Peru

Late Intermediate Period, 1000–1470 CE

Silver alloy

42.9 × 11.1 × 11.8 cm

2009.20.5

144. LIBATION VESSEL (QERO)

Inka, Peru

Late Horizon, 1470–1534 CE

Gold alloy

Height 7.5 cm, diameter 8.9 cm

TL.2009.20.241

145, 146. LIBATION VESSELS (QEROS)

Chancay, Central Coast, Peru

Late Intermediate Period, 1000–1470 CE

Silver

No. 145 (TL.2009.20.218): height 10.2 cm, diameter 11.2 cm

No. 146 (TL.2009.20.219): height 10.3 cm, diameter 10.8 cm

143

143

The *qero* was the principal ritual libation vessel among the peoples of ancient Peru, Bolivia, and northern Chile. This distinctive vessel form has ancient origins but became particularly prevalent during the Early Intermediate Period (100–600 CE). This dynamic time witnessed socio-political intensification and an increase in the numbers of political elites throughout the Andes, with an interconnected multiplication of aristocratic ceremonial events that emphasized hierarchy and authority. The ritual consumption of *chicha* (maize beer), the mildly alcoholic beverage traditionally served in *qeros*, was integral to these politically charged social events. These special drinking vessels often were made and used in pairs following the pan-Andean belief in reciprocity

144

145, 146

and communal sharing as a potent unifying principle of social practice. The silver pair (nos. 145, 146), which reportedly was excavated at the site of Huacho in the Chancay Valley, represents this key precept of Andean ideology. The Chancay elite maintained socio-political hierarchy, in part, by controlling the production and use of precious metal objects. Their tombs were furnished with gold and silver items as well as fine textiles woven with such elaborate techniques as brocade, gauze-weave, double-cloth, openwork fabrics, and painted cloth.[1]

Qero-like vessels are frequently depicted in scenes of ritual sacrifice, wherein they were used to contain sacrificial blood. The brimming vessel then was presented to the scene's key figure as a symbolic libation or was offered to the earth (Pacha Mama). A special goblet version of the *qero* is intimately connected to the "Sacrifice Ceremony" depicted on Moche painted ceramics, its shape being similar to the gold *qero* (no. 144).[2]

The political importance of the *qero* is underscored by its renderings on colossal stone portraits of mythical founders that punctuated the ceremonial heart of the imperial center of Tiwanaku, Bolivia. These impressive portrayals effuse elite authority by their size, the sacred symbols decorating the figures' elaborate clothing, and the presence of a snuff tray and a *qero* held by each founder.[3] Among the contemporary Wari in Peru, many portrayals of figures holding *qeros* depict a maize plant rising from the vessel. This iconic indicator suggests that the vessel was used to drink maize beer *(chichi)*, an important ritual libation and offering. The maize-*qero* dyad also makes reference to the vessel's pan-Andean use as the offering receptacle for blood to be poured on the ground during rites to ensure abundant crops.

These four libation vessels diverge from the typical *qero*'s beaker form. Their

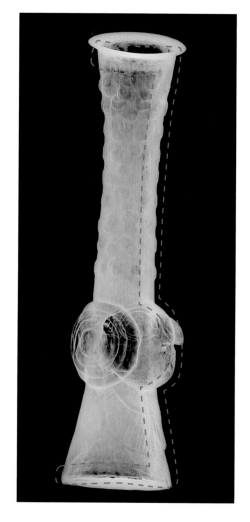

Fig. 1. In the x-ray image of no. 143, hammer marks are visible. Solder seams run down the front of the object and around the upper rim and the foot. The digital x-ray image was captured and viewed using GE Inspection Technologies' digital x-ray equipment and software.

precious metal material also segregates them from the usual ritual drinking vessel made of clay or wood.

The Chimú *qero* (no. 143) is unusually tall and embellished with a frontal face. The atypical shape of the gold goblet (no. 144) may be a provincial Inka vessel from the North or Central Coast.

Technical Commentary

No. 143: The main body of the vessel was created by hammering a single piece of silver sheet metal, possibly over a wooden form (fig. 1).[4] A vertical soldered seam extends the length of the vessel's front. The rim and base appear to be separate pieces of hammered metal that have been soldered to the main body, although it also may represent

post-excavation restoration. Some of the raised surface designs may have been worked in repoussé. Its composition is an alloy of 95% silver and 4.9% copper.[5] Damage to the vessel reflects extensive reworking and post-excavation re-forming (JA).

No. 144: The *qero* is made from two joined sections: the cup and the foot, each formed from hammered sheet (fig. 2). The thickness of the metal is non-uniform, measuring 0.048 mm at the rim and 0.025 mm at the foot. Both cup and foot are made from a gold alloy of similar purity, Au 73.2%, Cu 3%, Ag 23.5%,[6] suggesting that both pieces were created from the same sheet metal. The cup was likely formed by pressing the metal sheet into a wooden or stone mold. Wavy contours

of the lip indicate uneven stretching of the metal, which also could be a result of post-excavation re-forming. The foot was formed from a single, rectangular sheet with three horizontal cuts along the sides forming interlocking tabs that have been soldered. The resulting tube was hammered to the desired flared shape and attached to the bottom of the cup with solder (fig. 3). The solder, clearly visible on the vessel's exterior, is more silver in color than the gold sheet metal of the vessel (JA).[7]

Nos. 145, 146: These vessels were formed by hammering from a single sheet of metal; the flared foot of each is hollow and continuous with the main cup. Small, regular hammer marks are visible on the interior

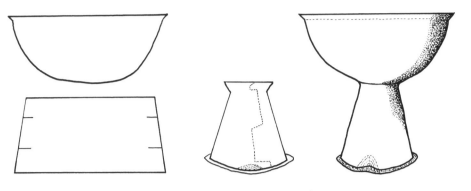

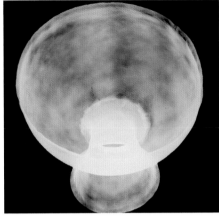

Fig. 2 (above). No. 144: Line drawing showing how *qero* was constructed.

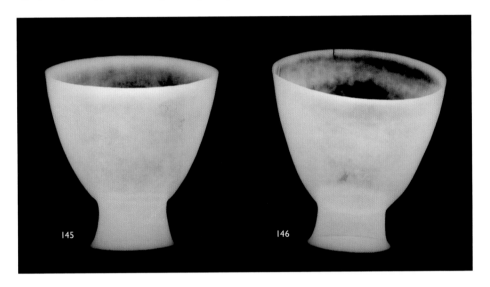

Fig. 3 (above). No. 144: Hammer marks are visible in the x-ray image, as is the solder used to join the foot to the cup. The digital x-ray images were captured and viewed using GE Inspection Technologies' digital x-ray equipment and software.

Fig. 4 (left). Nos. 145, 146: No seams or solder are visible in the x-ray image. There is a slight thickening of the metal at the rim of both vessels. The dark line on the vessels, where the flat bottom meets the side, may be caused by the fact that the metal is less dense here from being folded and worked, rather than indicating the presence of a seam.

and exterior surfaces of both objects and can be seen in the x-ray image (fig. 4). The rims are flat edged, and measure 0.13 to 0.18 mm thick. Both beakers are made from very pure silver, Ag 99.4%, Cu 0.5%, Au 0.2%; the flat section of each foot shows slightly higher copper levels (see note 5). Both show evidence of being re-formed after excavation. A small hole and cracks at the rim have developed in the weakened metal on no. 146, and the surface of both vessels is pitted and scratched (JA).

Notes

1. Moseley 2001, 259–60.

2. Los Angeles 1976, 172.

3. Denver 2004, 35.

4. Many Chimú silver beakers were made from a single piece of sheet silver by hammering the metal over carved wooden molds that are flat in the back and held in place with a wedge during hammering; others have solder seams along the back and bottom. New York 2000, 53.

5. Qualitative XRF analysis of a Lambayeque repoussé silver disk showed that the object was made from relatively pure silver. Copper and lead were present at low levels and gold present in trace amounts. Lechtman 1996b, 220 (technical description by H. Lechtman).

6. Composition data are reported as average weight percent. Though high in silver, the composition of no. 132 is similar to earlier Chimú pieces found to be an alloy of Au 76.2%, Cu 1%, Ag 21%. Ibid., 261.

7. The composition of the solder has not been analyzed. Ternary alloy (copper-silver-gold) and silver-copper solders of varied compositions have been documented on hammered gold Chimu and Lambayeque objects. Ibid., 228, 194.

147. RITUAL KNIFE (TUMI)

Moche, North Coast, Peru

Early Intermediate Period, 450–650 CE

Cast copper alloy

14.7 × 15.1 × 1.8 cm

TL.2009.20.255

148. STIRRUP-SPOUTED BOTTLE

Nasca, South Coast, Peru

Early Intermediate Period (Phase 6), 450–650 CE

Earthenware, burnished slip paint

Height 17 cm, diameter 16.8 cm

2009.20.28

These two very different objects are from contemporaneous but distant cultures, the Moche of Peru's northern coast and the Nasca who inhabited the southern coast. Although dissimilar in function, both pertain to the Andean theme of sacrifice and death as a religious act of regeneration and renewal. The small knife with crescent-shaped blade (a *tumi*) (no. 147) is a traditional Andean cutting implement that appears to have been the invention of the Moche during the Early Intermediate Period. *Tumis* are portrayed in Moche art being wielded by supernatural beings during decapitation rites and to threaten other beings; their quotidian use by humans, however, remains an open question.[1] This *tumi*'s shaft end is decorated with a three-

dimensional narrative of the impending sacrifice of a parrot, which perches on the arm of an attendant. The larger figure wields a hafted axe, its curved blade poised ready and aimed at the bird.

The expertly painted Nasca bottle (no. 148), with double spouts and bridge handle, represents the highest achievement in quality and pictorial complexity of Nasca pottery painting. Its imagery features the so-called Anthropomorphic Mythical Being, which may symbolize powerful spirits in nature.[2] At least fifteen subtypes of this spirit being are known, each perhaps corresponding to specific forces. A shared icon among them is the presence of trophy heads hanging at the waist (as seen here) or in close proximity to its mouth. On this vessel, a Nasca warrior

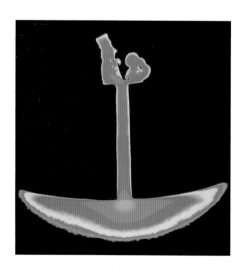

Fig. 1. Color x-ray image mapping density of metal: light pink indicates densest areas; green-blue indicates areas of least density

147

grasps the being's "tail" as if he has captured or is in control of the spirit force. The line of female heads around the vessel may be a symbolic representation of the earth.

The images on the *tumi* and the pottery vessel relate to the theme of sacrifice and agricultural fertility, the *tumi* being the quintessential ritual sacrifice tool. Among the Nasca, the severed head was likened to a seed from which sprang renewed life in the form of young plants; large caches of trophy heads found at Nasca sites are the remains of religious rites intended to ensure agricultural success. In short, the human trophy head was not only the most sacred of offerings to the spiritual forces of nature; they were also integral to the pan-Andean ideology of death and regeneration, being but two parts of the

same universal dyad.[3] Death, caused by sacrifice and decapitation, is not the end; rather it leads to rejuvenation and new life.

Technical Commentary

No. 147: This sacrificial knife was made using the lost-wax casting technique, although it is unclear whether the shaft and the blade were cast as one piece, or in two pieces that were then fused together. Both sections are solid, but x-radiography indicates a significant increase in the thickness of the metal where the blade meets the cylindrical shaft (fig. 1). This may be the result of the attachment of the two pieces after casting. The variation in density shown in the x-ray image reflects both the thickness of the metal at this shaft-blade joint as well as the degree

of thinning of the metal along the edge of the blade as a result of mineralization. The x-ray image also shows substantial porosity in the nose of the human figure, which may be the result of a repair or fill.

The original copper alloy surface has been completely obscured by a thick layer of corrosion products resulting from long-term burial. Though other related examples appear to have been gilded, no evidence of gilding was found on this object (BF).

Notes

1. Lechtman 1996b, 209.

2. Proulx 2006, 62.

3. Ibid., 8–9, 102–3.

148

APPROACHES TO AUTHENTICATION

JULIE LAUFFENBURGER

By collecting and studying artifacts, museums and research institutions seek to understand and disseminate information about cultures and peoples, past and present. The Bourne Collection, a gift to the Walters Art Museum of some three hundred artifacts from ancient Mesoamerica, Central, and Andean South America, has provided conservators and curators with a rare opportunity to study a large number of assembled objects. While this research will continue for years to come, contributing to studies of ancient society and history and cross-cultural technological exchanges, our study of the Bourne Collection has already added to our knowledge of the materials and artistic techniques used by ancient American artists from Mexico to Peru. These observations have allowed us to recognize objects whose forming techniques are not consistent with ancient American craftsmanship, bringing into question their authenticity. Studying objects of uncertain origin also provides invaluable data for future studies by conservators, curators, and materials scientists by adding to the body of knowledge in the scientific study of materials used in ancient American art.

The history of collecting the art of the ancient Americas is well documented in the notes and diaries of early collectors.[1] It began at roughly the same moment that colonialism ended in Mexico during the Mexican war of independence (1810–1821), the ancient artworks serving as icons of the emerging new nation. The first documented forgeries appeared in Mexico at around the same time.[2] For more than two hundred years thereafter, supply and demand for ancient American art rose and fell. Illegal looting of archaeological sites fed periods of increased demand for artifacts well into the late twentieth century. Forgers quickly followed and produced imitations of artifacts almost as soon as they were unearthed. The presence of so many modern copies of ancient artifacts and the lack of secure provenance for many others challenge our ability to establish the authenticity of a given work with certainty. Current efforts focus on a variety of data—a piece's imagery, form, materials composition, and manufacturing techniques—to aid in the process of authentication. While collecting objects from the ancient Americas is of fairly long standing, the authentication of these works is more recent, hampered by the complicated history of acquiring ancient art of the Americas.

Many of the early spurious objects have found their way into public and private collections, and many undoubtedly remain to be discovered. Fakes are ubiquitous, and the presence of such objects in a collection is not necessarily a reflection of poor connoisseurship or a lack of understanding of the materials. It is the dearth of large numbers of comparative examples of secure provenance that makes the authentication process so difficult, as well as the fact that many of the artifacts illustrated in early publications are untrustworthy. Most major collectors have fallen prey to highly expert forgers whose broad knowledge of ancient materials and techniques makes their work difficult to discern. Some forgeries are difficult to detect even with sophisticated analytical techniques. Such discoveries are the result of systematic, collaborative research by art historians, conservators, scientists, and archaeologists. For example, recent studies of purportedly ancient precious metal objects in the Museo del Oro in Lima, Peru, found that 4,237 of 4,349 were modern (identifying only 112 as authentic works).[3] Further, two celebrated rock crystal skulls, once prominently displayed at the British Museum and at the Museum of Natural History of the Smithsonian Institution, Washington, DC, as Aztec masterpieces, were recently identified as nineteenth-century fakes.[4]

The study of fakes and forgeries is aided by the increasing number of good publications on artifacts of secure provenance.[5] Unfortunately, most such publications do not include technical data concerning materials analysis or production techniques.[6] The opportunity to conduct detailed technical studies of most private collections is rarely available. As a result, collectors (and some museums) rely on information from art dealers to support the authenticity of their holdings. The Bourne Collection provided the Walters Art Museum with an excellent opportunity to initiate studies of each artifact to ascertain condition and authenticity.

Our authentication studies began with the identification of the materials used to manufacture each object. We then sought to understand how the materials were used in the object's construction. Evidence of some techniques can be seen with the naked eye, while others require high-power magnification. Features that cannot be seen with the naked eye can sometimes be detected through investigative techniques such as ultraviolet-light examination and x-radiography or computed tomography (CT), which is helpful in the examination of pottery fabrication. X-ray fluorescence spectroscopy (XRF) was used to identify metal alloy components; thermoluminscence (TL) and carbon 14 analysis were used to date ceramics and wooden objects, respectively. We came across objects whose date of manufacture was ambiguous or that had authentic components but whose overall composition was suspect; others had been so heavily restored

that we initially questioned their authenticity. A recurring question arose in these instances: when is an object so completely transformed by modern restoration that it no longer is a product of antiquity?

Technical research at the Walters Art Museum has focused on three major categories of materials represented in the Bourne Collection: metals (primarily gold alloys), ceramics, and stone.

METALS

The authentication of metalwork depends on an understanding of the materials and techniques used by specific cultures and in specific regions. Ancient American metallurgy, which has been studied extensively,[7] is set apart from that of other ancient world cultures by its distinctive and pervasive use of alloys of gold and copper or gold, copper, and silver (tumbaga). Alloying—the mixing of two or more metals in a molten state to exploit differences in color and mechanical properties—was, of course, not unique to the Americas. But ancient American metallurgy is distinguished by the pervasive use of the purposeful creation of gold-enriched surfaces on alloys, a technology not as pervasive among most other ancient societies.

Several interpretations have been proposed to account for the prevalence of gold alloys among ancient American cultures. The artisans observed, perhaps accidentally, that an alloy of gold and copper melts at a lower temperature than does gold alone, and that such an alloy is both easier to cast and stronger than pure gold.[8] It is likely, moreover, that gold, when present within the alloy, had some spiritual significance that could not be attained with gilded surfaces alone.[9]

Ancient American metalworkers incorporated gold, prized for its resistance to corrosion and its ductile qualities, into base metals to create the appearance of pure gold. The technique of gilding and silvering base metals such as copper was expertly used by Andean cultures, most notably the Moche. Differently colored metals were often juxtaposed to achieve particular aesthetic effects.[10]

In most cases the golden color of tumbaga objects was achieved by a process of enriching the gold metal at the object's surface. Other techniques also were used to achieve this effect, including the application of a discrete gold layer on the object's surface by foil gilding, fusion gilding, or electrochemical replacement plating.[11] The technique of mercury amalgam gilding, which was developed in both Asia and the Near East, is noticeably absent in metalwork from the ancient Americas.[12] In the ancient Americas, surface enrichment of tumbaga alloys was generally achieved by depletion gilding, a process in which surfaces are depleted of copper and silver, leaving an enriched gold alloy. Through a repeated process of working, annealing, and pickling of the copper oxides formed on the surface of an alloy, the copper content naturally diminishes. Finally, a paste suffused with either mineral or organic acids and heated in contact with the metal over a period of time results in a surface in which the silver and copper have been substantially diminished.[13] When burnished and heated, the initially porous enriched gold layer is structurally bound to the gold alloy matrix. The resulting gold layer is quite thin (typically between 3 to 20 microns), but an increased proportion of gold in the alloy due to partial removal of the base metals extends further into the metal matrix. Because the layer of gold is thin, depletion-gilded surfaces are easily worn away with use—wear, repeated cleanings, or abrasion—revealing a more copper-colored alloy beneath the enriched surface (fig. 1).

The color of tumbaga varies considerably depending on the original alloy and extent of surface enrichment (see fig. 2), but color alone cannot confirm the presence of an enriched gold surface; such a determination requires specific analytical tools. For example, microscopic samples from tumbaga objects, viewed in cross section, show an alloy that contains

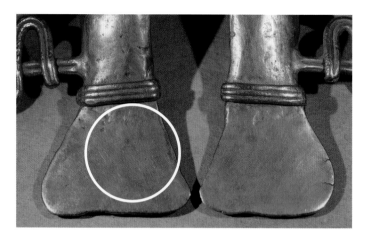

Fig. 1. Detail showing enriched gold surfaces with copper-rich surfaces beneath, Diquís human effigy pendant, cat. no. 103

gold while displaying higher levels of gold at the surface.[14] The absence of a visibly enriched surface at this microscopic level is reason for closer scrutiny of the object because this feature is inconsistent with the expected production techniques seen in many ancient American gold alloy artifacts.[15]

Using published studies of the range of gold alloys in ancient American metallurgy for reference, we used nondestructive x-ray fluorescence spectroscopy (XRF) to analyze gold alloys in the Bourne Collection. It was expected that XRF would reveal anomalies by showing differences in the expected composition of the alloys.[16] In only one case, however—a pair of miniature Sicán mask ornaments (fig. 3)—did a qualitative study of the alloy's composition show anomalies. The masks were composed of a copper and zinc alloy with a layer of gold applied to the surface. Zinc was not used as an alloying metal in ancient artifacts from Mesoamerica and South America. Therefore, its presence in the alloy used to make these masks cast doubt as to their authenticity.[17] The absence of mercury, moreover, indicated that the gold layer had not been applied by the ancient technique of amalgam gilding but instead by the modern technique of electroplating.

The gold pieces in the Bourne Collection, the majority from Central and Andean South America, contain varying proportions of gold, silver, and copper. Some have been determined to be of modern origin, although, interestingly, these are composed of the same three metals present in ancient tumbaga objects. We may conclude that the forgers were

Fig. 2. Compare the rich gold color of the Veraguas shamanic effigy pendant, cat. no. 110, with the copper tone of the Diquís human effigy pendant, cat. no. 103.

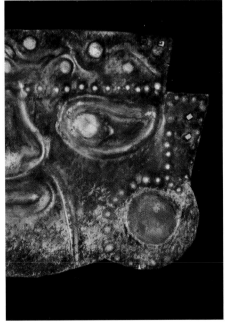

Fig. 3. Front and back of Sicán-style adornment, checklist no. 145, showing brassy color of reverse

Fig. 4. Stone metalsmithing tools. Courtesy the Museo del Oro, Banco de la Republica, Bogotá, Colombia (Photo Clark M. Rodríguez)

knowledgeable about the composition of ancient American alloys.[18] In a few instances, however, XRF revealed alloys whose percentages of specific metals were out of range of comparable data sets.

Both hammering and casting technologies were employed in the ancient Americas, with regional preferences rooted in cultural traditions and influences. Sheet metal, produced using finely crafted stone hammers and anvils, flourished among ancient Andean cultures in Ecuador, Colombia, and Peru. A metalsmith's tool kit in the collection of the Museo del Oro in Cartagena, Colombia (fig. 4) is deceptively simple in appearance; these tools were capable of producing extraordinarily thin and uniform sheets of gold or silver, and they were handed down as prized possessions through generations of craftsmen.

Sicán funerary masks from Peru (see checklist nos. 149, 150) attest to the high level of the metalworkers' expertise. These masks, which measure up to 46 × 25 cm, were made from sheet metal hammered to a thickness of only 0.5–0.6 mm, and the variation in sheet thickness within a single mask is less than 0.1 mm.[19] Burnishing implements of bone, stone, corn husk, and wood charged with loose abrasives were used to achieve a final polish. The marks left behind by these

ancient techniques are subtle, varying in orientation and in size (fig. 5). These telltale marks are unlike those left by modern machine polishing, which creates a regular pattern of fine lines, as seen in the marks found on the surface of a gold alloy belt rattle thought to be from northern Peru (fig. 6).

Archaeological records provide no evidence for the working of iron in the ancient New World prior to colonialization.[20] Nor was true bronze, an alloy of copper and tin, used for the production of tools to fabricate gold alloy sheet, although early Peruvian cultures did make use of soft copper chisels. Instead, tumbaga chisels, hardened by successive cold-working of the metal, were used to delineate forms in sheet metal and to create relief in repoussé.[21] Because tools leave behind characteristic marks or patterns, the knowledge of the types of tools used in antiquity can help to distinguish between ancient and modern objects. An enlarged photographic detail from a purportedly Moche gold object, for example, shows sharp incised tool marks and jagged cut edges (see fig. 6). This evidence points to the use of modern hard-metal tools and modern mechanical polishing techniques.[22] Other modern tools, including metal shears (used to cut sheet metal) and metal tubes (used to punch circular shapes) also leave distinctive signatures, as is clearly seen in a Calima-style nose pendant (fig. 7).

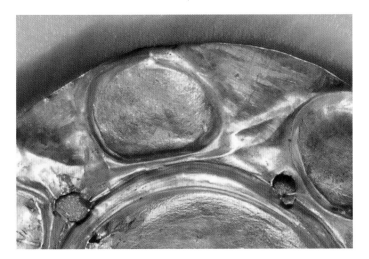

Fig. 5. Detail of subtle surface modulation on a Panamanian gold ornament from the University of Pennsylvania Museum of Archaeology and Anthropology (40-13-13)

Fig. 6. Detail of overall machine polish marks and sharp, jagged edges created by metal tools on a Moche-style gold ornament from Peru, checklist no. 139

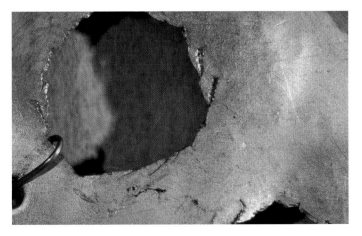

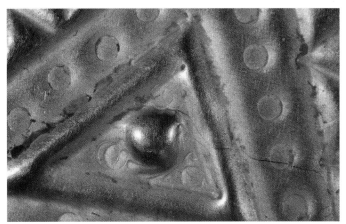

Fig. 7. Detail of roughly cut openings (left) and tubular punch marks (right) on a Calima-style nose ornament from Colombia, checklist no. 124

Interestingly, the metal used to produce this ornament shows delamination typical of the deterioration found on ancient metals thinned by successive hammer blows. The metal sheet also contains small silvery colored platinoid inclusions, visible only with magnification. These inclusions are found in alluvial gold sources typically used by the ancient Americans as a source of gold.[23] This is an unfortunate example of the use of ancient sheet metal, perhaps originally undecorated, that was cut down and repurposed in modern times.[24]

The study of ancient construction techniques as applied to our study of the Bourne Collection has helped to confirm the authenticity of a pair of Moche ear spools.[25] Each ear spool is constructed of five separate sheet elements, mechanically joined with tabs, slots, and crimping. All of these techniques are characteristic of ancient Andean metalworking. X-radiography reveals how the individual elements were joined (fig. 8). A separately cast ring of spheres is held in place by a flange; close examination of the spheres shows

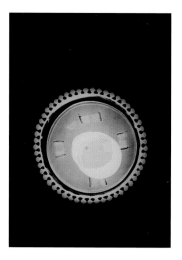

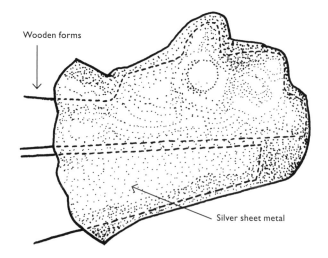
Wooden forms

Silver sheet metal

Fig. 8. X-radiograph of Moche spools, cat. no. 140, from the side and end-on showing sheet metal construction technique, including both mechanical and soldering methods of attachment

Fig. 9. Illustration showing working of sheet metal over wooden forms to create traditional Chimú silver vessels

slight variation in size and shape. Tabs along the spool's post are secured by a gold-alloy solder that melted at a temperature lower than that of the surrounding metal; this, too, is characteristic of Andean metallurgy.[26] Because of the similarity between the color of the gold-alloy solders and that of the ear spools, the solder seams are difficult to discern, as they often are in authentic objects. Soft solders—which are mixtures of lead and tin, both white-colored metals—were not used in the pre-Conquest Americas.

Hollow vessels constructed of sheet metal were often formed over templates of stone and wood. The Chimú of northern Peru were known for their elaborate effigy vessels, like the silver beaker seen in cat. no. 143. Impressive examples are constructed from a single sheet of silver, expertly hammered and shaped over wooden forms (fig. 9). Vessels made using traditional methods have no more than one solder seam; silver vessels assembled from multiple sections are therefore suspect.[27] Wire, produced by hammering and other techniques such as block- and strip-twisting common to Europe, the Near East, and Asia, is frequently used to secure decorative embellishments on ancient American artifacts.[28] Wire that is rectangular in section, hand formed, and likely made from sheet metal can be seen in an ancient example from Colombia (fig. 10a). Drawn wire, produced by pulling or "drawing"

metal through successively smaller circular openings, displaying straight, parallel lines along its length (fig. 10b); the technique is not documented in the ancient Americas. Wire of this type, then, indicates modern manufacture.

Casting traditions, as opposed to sheet metal production, were especially dominant among the ancient cultures of Mesoamerica and Central America. A progressively sophisticated process evolved through time, from the use of open stone molds, to two-part clay molds, and later to the technique of lost-wax casting.[29] Alloys for casting are significantly higher in copper than those used to produce sheet metal, the ancient metalsmiths preferring these higher copper alloys because they have a lower melting point and greater hardness than those with smaller percentages of copper.[30] Generally cast in one piece using the lost-wax process, animal or figural pendants, such as the adornment from Costa Rica (fig. 11), often show evidence of the manipulation of the wax into signature ribbons of "false-filigree." In true filigree, which is common in jewelry from ancient Greece and Egypt, individual metal wires are arranged in decorative patterns and then soldered in place. In New World false filigree, these patterns were made in the wax model and then incorporated in the casting.[31] Metal tabs or bridges from the wax original indicate the construction methods used to create the wax model.

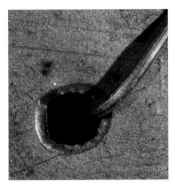

Fig. 10A (left). Detail of hand-wrought gold wire from Colombian ornament from the University of Pennsylvania Museum of Archaeology and Anthropology (SA2806)

Fig. 10B (right). Detail of parallel lines on drawn wire from a Colima-style nose ornament, checklist no. 124

Fig. 11. Detail, reverse of Diquís human effigy pendant, cat. no. 103, showing wax construction techniques and vestiges of original sprue system

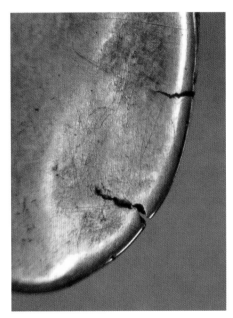

Fig. 12. This detail of cat. no. 103 shows branched surface cracking typical of embrittlement observed in ancient, worked gold-copper-silver alloys.

Typically, little work was done to these objects after casting, aside from the necessary removal of remnants of the casting process.[32] Minor flaws were generally left untouched, and the backs of cast figures are often completely unfinished and have a rough pebbly surface (see fig. 11).

Though many tumbaga alloys show cracking and corrosion typical of archaeological metals (fig. 12), not all show significant evidence of burial corrosion; many authentic ancient objects are almost entirely free of corrosion. This is due variously to the composition of the alloys, the specific archaeological context, or undocumented post-excavation treatments. Typically, evidence of wear is used to substantiate the ancient origin of a piece (see fig. 2), but that evidence alone is insufficient to determine an object's age; some pieces were cast expressly for funerary use and thus exhibit no wear patterns.

The method of fabrication is sometimes extremely difficult to discern in forgeries. For example, a small figurine from Colombia revealed some unusual features (fig. 13). Comparable objects from the Quimbaya region of central Colombia are either hollow lost-wax casts of unusual heft or made of fairly thick sheet metal hammered over a wooden form.[33] In this object, an opening and overlap of metal on the interior of the figurine's leg suggest sheet construction; the metal used to create this object is extremely thin. Yet it does not exhibit delamination of the surface that is typically seen in ancient hammered sheet metal. The presence of a series of small holes in the metal recesses near the ears and eyes raise further questions about its method of fabrication. These holes look like the result of problems with casting rather than the kind of marks resulting from sheet work. Microscopic examination along the edge of an area of overlapping metal hidden between the legs revealed an unusual formation. The metal resembles small floral heads of cauliflower, reminiscent of the way metal is deposited during the process of creating electroform copies of metal artifacts (see fig. 13). Electroforming, unknown until the 1840s, is a technique by which metal is plated onto the surface of a conductive mold. The presence of the unusual "coliform" structure, the holes in the eyes where the electroform did not completely fill in, and the extremely thin metal wall are all indications of manufacture through the nineteenth-century technique of electroforming.[34]

CERAMICS

Indicators of age in ceramics include use-wear patterns, burial incrustations and root marks, and the presence of manganese staining—a black, variably shaped stain that can form as a result of specific burial conditions (particularly present in ancient West Mexican pottery).[35] These features have been more or less successfully imitated by modern forgers, which complicates our investigation of ancient American ceramics, particularly those from West Mexico.

Fired ceramics offer the possibility of dating by means of thermoluminescence (TL), which is one of the few investigatory techniques available that provides a specific date range of production for a pottery object. TL dating is based on the fact that some clay minerals absorb energy or radiation at a predictable rate. When clay is fired, the absorbed energy is dissipated, and the clay minerals begin to reabsorb energy. This energy can be measured from a small ceramic sample, and the approximate date when the ceramic was last fired can be calculated.[36] The technique, however, is not applicable to all types of ceramics, and TL dating cannot distinguish between original and after-firings, a technique used in some early restorations.

TL analysis was used to confirm the date of manufacture of a pair of Zapotec urns, revealing a firing date between

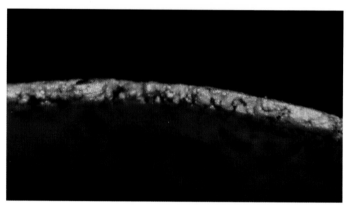

Fig. 13. Detail of porosities in facial area of Quimbaya-style female effigy, checklist no. 123. Magnified image of "coliform" texture on interior.

550 and 950 CE, which accords with the urns' stylistic characteristics. Because each urn was intact and there were no major restorations, TL authentication was a straightforward process. More commonly, however, archaeological ceramics are broken, either as part of ancient rituals or because of the burial environment. Objects often are reassembled from multiple fragments, and restorers may incorporate fragments from more than one original artifact as well as adding substantial amounts of restoration material. Cases like this require careful examination to determine the number of TL samples necessary and the locations from which to extract the tiny ceramic sample in order to establish the date of manufacture. In the case of another large Zapotec figural urn (cat. no. 30), five TL samples had to be taken in order to ensure accurate results. As documented in our condition drawing (fig. 14), the vessel was restored from many fragments and

incorporated large amounts of modern restoration material. The drawing illustrates the complexity of the restoration and highlights the importance of confirming that stylistically diagnostic elements are original.[37]

While scientific tools like TL dating advance our understanding of ancient cultures, they have also been used by forgers to deceive collectors. Attempts at artificially aging ceramics using the principle of thermoluminescence and stored energy within the clay body have been documented.[38] Personal communication with museum colleagues confirmed the current practice of such artificial "aging" of ceramics in regions of China.[39]

One of the common challenges in interpreting ancient American ceramics is their pervasive over-restoration. Close examination of a ceramic surface in ultraviolet light will often reveal surface coatings, repairs, and replacement parts. Natural resins and many adhesives fluoresce under ultraviolet light, whereas ceramic surfaces generally do not. However, some restoration materials do not fluoresce, so the lack of fluorescence is not necessarily evidence of authenticity. In some instances, the restorer's nonfluorescent paint covers substantial portions of original surfaces in an attempt to make a broken figure appear intact.

X-radiography is a powerful tool that can be used to identify breaks and repairs. This high-energy imaging technique identifies structure beneath the surface by revealing differences in density of materials. X-radiography must be used sparingly and cautiously, however, because the energy from x-rays can skew subsequent TL dating analyses. Although the end results are often aesthetically pleasing, restoration poses difficulty when the restored surface is interpreted as a product of antiquity. For example, overpaint concealed numerous breaks and completely covered the original surfaces of a beautiful Olmec figurine (fig. 15). An ethical conservation treatment, which would maintain the original aesthetics of the ancient artwork, would integrate the missing pieces by

Fig. 14. Zapotec figural urn, cat. no. 30, highlighting assembled fragments and associated fill material

Fig. 15. Reverse of Olmec infantile figure, cat. no. 10, before and after removal of modern overpaint, revealing network of original, adjoining fragments

filling only the losses along the ceramic fragments, leaving the original surfaces in plain sight.

Establishing a body of knowledge in ceramic technology is essential to providing a standard against which other artifacts may be measured. Research has confirmed that ancient American pottery vessels and sculpture were made without the use of a potter's wheel for forming vessels, although simple turntables were used for finishing hand-built pieces.[40] Ancient American ceramics were either completely hand formed or produced with molds. The famous Moche stirrup vessels and ornate figural sculptures from Veracruz were formed from molds. Mold-made elements were also incorporated into hand-built vessels, exemplified by the repetitive decorative appliqués on Maya incense burners (fig. 16).

Coil construction and slab construction, used alone or in combination, were the main methods for fabricating ceramic vessels and sculpture in the ancient Americas. Supplementing these basic building techniques were secondary finishing processes such as scraping (to thin and compress the clay walls) and paddle and anvil—a technique in which a wooden paddle is applied to the exterior of a clay vessel wall against a corresponding form on the interior. Evidence of primary building techniques is often obscured by these finishing processes. Facial features, such as noses, and decorative elements, such as bracelets and earrings, were frequently modeled separately and attached to figural sculpture. Additional decoration was made by incising lines and patterns into the clay prior to

Fig. 16. Detail showing mold made elements from Classic period Maya incense burner, checklist no. 80

firing. Clay surfaces were colored and decorated by the application of colored slip (a highly refined clay slurry pigmented with mineral oxides), reduction firings to reveal resist-painted designs, and the application of paints after firing. Glazes, essentially layers of colored glass melted at high temperatures in an enclosed kiln, were not used by ancient American ceramists.

The Bourne Collection is especially rich in figural sculpture from ancient West Mexico.[41] Among these is a fine group of five figures from Lagunillas (fig. 17). These represent three different Lagunillas styles and thus provide a good reference group for our understanding of ancient production techniques. They were examined with visible and ultraviolet light and x-radiography. In addition to documenting condition, x-radiography can also be used to investigate methods of fabrication; it revealed a distinctive cloudlike pattern on three of the figures (fig. 18).[42] This "cloud" pattern suggests a direct manipulation of the clay without much finishing of the interior clay wall. Upon closer inspection of the radiograph, a pattern of horizontal banding can be seen in the figures' legs. This is a result of the progressive building up of the clay wall, which indicates the use of the coil method to form the figure. Also visible are variations in the thickness of the clay wall, which indicate hand building; these variations appear in the image as relative whiteness or grayness, the thicker walls being the white areas.

The x-radiograph images also indicate a fair amount of pinching and manipulation of the coil, perhaps done entirely by hand or supplemented by the use of the paddle and anvil technique. The three sculptures most closely related stylistically (cat. nos. 49, 50, and 51) are distinguished by a similarly homogeneous and well-levigated clay body, evidence of a high level of clay paste processing. The Protoclassic form seen in cat. no. 148 shows a similarly refined clay body, whereas the clay body of checklist no. 34 shares similarities with Jalisco ceramics that are part of the Walters Art Museum's ongoing study of West Mexican ceramics.[43]

All five figures in the Lagunillas group are hollow formed, with solid arms attached as coils. The ceramic wall is quite even, and the three Type C figures have a thickening in the

Fig. 17. Group of Lagunillas ceramics: (left to right) cat. nos. 49, 51, 50, 48, and checklist no. 34

neck wall that may have been necessary to support their fairly heavy heads during construction. Remnants of an interior core material are visible in the color-enhanced x-ray image seen in figure 19. Ongoing work using computed tomography (CT scanning) may provide additional information about how the figures were constructed.[44] Material trapped on the interior of the lower leg of checklist no. 34 appears to be a remnant of its original construction, perhaps a temporary core used as a support during the manufacturing. This support material was partially removed prior to firing, but traces remain in hard-to-reach sections. Evidence of minor reworking of the clay at the top of the head suggests that the core material was removed through an opening in this area. The x-radiograph shows the clay wall on either side of the head tapering toward what was originally an opening. The hole was closed after the core was removed but before the figure was fired. This final, thin addition of clay can be seen bridging the ends of the tapered clay walls (fig. 20). We have observed this type of core in other figural ceramics from West Mexico (see nos. 35, 44, and checklist no. 37).

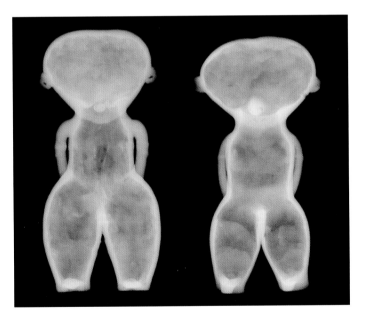
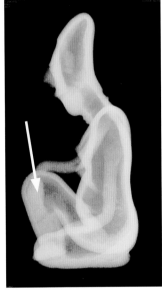
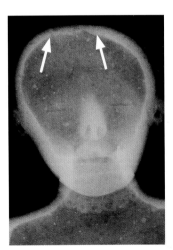

Fig. 18. Digital x-radiographs of Lagunillas figurines, cat. nos. 49, 50

Fig. 19. Colored digital x-radiograph of a Lagunillas figurine, checklist no. 34, showing internal core material

Fig. 20. Detail digital x-radiograph image of top of the head from a Lagunillas figurine, checklist no. 34, showing area of previous opening at center of the head

Figural form and body ornament are rendered in both additive and subtractive processes on the Lagunillas figures. Lumps of clay (visible in x-radiographs) were used to fashion the nose and ears, and subtle patterns of incised lines were used to represent the figures' hair. Surface ornamentation was often part of the West Mexican potter's art. Color and pattern were created with broad washes of colored slips and finely painted designs of contrasting colored slips. While the palette of applied slips used to decorate West Mexican ceramics is limited, the artists' combined use of paint and incision results in visually dynamic surfaces. Cat. nos. 49, 50, and 51 are distinguished by the use of broad areas of red and white slip.[45] The slip-decorated surfaces serve as a backdrop for details painted in a dense black slip. Additional decorative techniques include resist painting, a technique in which areas that are to remain unpainted are coated with some type of waxy material that will "resist" the slip application, creating a design that is rendered as negative space against a painted background. Resist painting can be seen on the leg of one of the Lagunillas sculptures (fig. 21)

STONE

William Spratling, an American artist who lived and worked in Mexico during the twentieth century, remarked on the early influx of spurious artifacts in the market for ancient American art: "Demand from affluent city folk for coarse examples of stone sculpture led the rural poor and not so poor to begin to fashion copies, fakes of pre-Conquest artifacts."[46] Many of these sculptures continue to circulate into the art market and have found their way into museum collections and publications featuring the art of the ancient Americas. Thus our comparative sample of ancient stone artworks is problematic. The authentication of stone through scientific analysis is further complicated by the fact that the available dating methods can assess only the geological age of the stone, not the date of an object's manufacture. Therefore, to a greater extent than in other media, artistic style and iconography remain the best means of determining authenticity. Yet again, the problematic nature of much of the comparative material renders authentication a difficult process. Here, the collaborative work of

Fig. 21. Detail showing resist painting pattern on Lagunillas figurine, cat. no. 48

conservators, scientists, and art historians is particularly crucial to an accurate assessment.

Jadeite is a very hard stone found in the ancient Americas, being a pyroxene family sodium-aluminum silicate (as opposed to softer jade, a nephrite of the calcium and magnesium-rich amphibole mineral actinolite and found primarily in Asia). Jadeite was carved into all manner of body adornments, figurines, and ritual objects by many cultures in Mesoamerica and Central America. Current scholarship identifies the Motagua Fault in southern Guatemala as the primary source for the stone.[47] Modern workshops in Antigua and Guatemala City are making use of the same sources to manufacture spurious artifacts.[48] This makes it impossible to assign a date of manufacture exclusively on the basis of the source of the mineral used to create an artifact.[49] Consequently, the authentication of jadeite artifacts is rooted in stylistic analysis and the study of surface features, including tool marks and weathering or wear patterns.

Ancient American stone workers fashioned jadeite and similar minerals such as serpentinite into artifacts without the benefit of implements (such as hard metal tools) or abrasives harder than the stone they shaped. The primary forming technique was the slow, methodical grinding and polishing of the surface with such tools as fire-hardened wood, strings fashioned from vegetal fibers, and hollow reeds charged with loose abrasives such as sand or garnet.[50] Rudimentary lathes were also likely used, and finely incised lines were created with obsidian tools.

Large jadeite fragments were thinned into usable blanks by a combination of hand drilling (with the point of a rotating stick) and hand "sawing" using string and abrasive pulled back and forth across a stone surface.[51] Working from each end of the stone toward its interior, the string saw was used until the point of attachment between the two halves of stone was sufficiently thin. Then the stone was tapped into two sections and separated. This technique left behind a small raised

line of fractured stone, referred to as a lenticular fracture, on the back of many jadeite artifacts (fig. 22).

Modern jade carvers and forgers initially use power tools. These result in extremely flat and angular surfaces like those seen on the legs of checklist no. 123. In an attempt to mimic patinas that form naturally on stone as it ages, forgers frequently apply darkened coatings to freshly cut surfaces (fig. 23). Drilled holes often provide important clues concerning authenticity. Those made with modern tools are typically smooth and have sharp edges, whereas ancient drill holes have horizontal parallel lines and often flare at their opening due to the inevitable wobble of hand-held tools and rudimentary lathes. Yet forgers can easily obliterate evidence of modern metal tools, and thus the study of stone tool marks must rely on specific expertise and sophisticated equipment.[52] The final, high polish typical of ancient American jadeite artifacts was

Fig. 22. Detail of lenticular fracture on reverse of Mayan green stone pendant, cat. no. 91

Fig. 23. Detail image of planar and regular machine saw marks and artificially stained surfaces, checklist no. 1

achieved with fine-polishing, often using such smooth and highly compacted stones as hematite. The technique resulted in a surface sheen that is somewhat irregular. Thus a highly polished, uniform surface may indicate the use of a modern polishing machine.

"Forgeries are better than the real thing because they fit our ideas better."[53] This comment by Esther Pasztory, a pre-eminent art historian at Columbia University, goes to the heart of the difficulty in identifying fakes in the corpus of art of the ancient Americas. She highlights the fact that forgers do not simply copy original pieces. Instead, they combine ancient elements with newly invented ones that speak directly to the modern aesthetic. The authentication of ancient objects is a complicated process that must include the collaborative efforts of experts from a variety of humanistic and scientific disciplines. Our understanding of ancient societies is achieved primarily through the interpretation of the material culture they left behind. The museum, as a repository of collections of artifacts, makes possible the study of these materials. Knowledge gleaned from careful analysis of objects, whether ancient or not, reveals technical and aesthetic facets of manufacture that are useful in our common pursuit of understanding ancient historical processes and the world's artistic heritage.

NOTES

1. Walsh 2005.

2. Coe 1993; Walsh 2005.

3. "Fakes in Peru's Gold Museum," *Art Newspaper* 13, no. 121 (2002).

4. Sax et al. 2008.

5. See, for example, Boone 1978 and Pasztory 2002.

6. Bruhns and Kelker 2010.

7. Lechtman 1971; Lechtman 1973; Bray 1993; D. Scott 1994.

8. Emmerich 1984, 162. The melting point of pure gold (Au) is 1,063° C. The melting point of pure copper (Cu) is 1,083° C. The melting point of an alloy of Au 82% and Cu 18% is 878° C.

9. Lechtman 1986.

10. Alva and Donnan 1993; Schorsch 1998.

11. D. Scott 2000.

12. This process involves applying a liquid mixture of gold and mercury to a base metal, which is then heated to drive off the mercury and leave the gold behind; the use of this technique is indicated by traces of mercury on a gold surface. Lechtman 1971, 26.

13. Bray 1993.

14. D. Scott 1991b, 116.

15. Three metallographic cross sections were taken from three different objects in the Bourne collection (checklist nos. 124, 139, 148). In all three cases examination with scanning electron/energy-dispersive x-ray spectroscopy (SEM-EDS), revealed no significant enrichment of the surfaces. In fact, no documentable variation in the composition of the metal was observed. However in one case, (cat.oo), there was evidence of inter-granular surface corrosion similar to that observed on other ancient metals, supporting the antiquity of this metal. Richard Newman from the Scientific Research Laboratory at the Museum of Fine Arts, Boston, examined metal cross sections of three gold artifacts prepared by Glenn Gates and Jessie Arista from the Walters Art Museum. Using scanning electron microscopy/energy-dispersive x-ray spectrometry (SEM-EDS), Dr. Newman conducted line scans, x-ray mapping, and small-area analyses to determine overall alloy composition and homogeneity of metal composition, including whether surface depletion or enrichment had taken place. In all three samples, no significant variations in the composition of the metal were observed.

16. Alloys appropriate for specific cultures and time periods are documented in Fleming 1992; Rovira 1994; D. Scott 1994; Shimada, Griffin, and Gordus 2000; Chapdelaine, Kennedy, and Uceda Castillo 2001; and Harrison and Beaubien 2010. Qualitative and quantitative x-ray fluorescence was performed by Glenn Gates using an ARTAX spectrophotometer equipped with a Rhodium tube.

17. In fact, little or no Zn is found in even trace element analysis of ancient metalwork from the regions. See trace elements analysis reports from copper alloy beads from Colombia: D. Scott 1980; D. Scott 1986, 39; see also Jackson 2007. Harriet Beaubien, head conservator at the Museum Conservation Institute at the Smithsonian Institution, is quoted in the article, noting that the presence of zinc as an intentional alloy component in ancient American gold is grounds for suspicion.

18. Reports for the metal alloys analyzed by Glenn Gates are located in the object conservation files at the Walters Art Museum. Data for the objects included in the catalogue appear with their entries.

19. Shimada, Griffin, and Gordus 2000.

20. Lechtman 1980. Though iron smelting was not known in the ancient New World, an ancient iron ore mine used for hematite or ochre as a source for pigments was recently discovered in the Peruvian Andes. See Hearn 2008.

21. Emmerich and Lothrop 1954.

22. Compare with images of gold work from Alva and Donnan 1993.

23. D. Scott and Bray 1980.

24. Comments summarized from observations made by Anna Bennett.

25. See Lechtman, Erlij, and Barry 1982, 12, for a photograph illustrating the fabrication techniques for a Moche earspool from Loma Negra.

26. Emmerich 1984, 168.

27. For a clear illustration of the technique used to produce Chimú silver beakers, see Emmerich 1984, 31 fig. 38.

28. J. Scott 1991.

29. Emmerich 1984, 160.

30. Harrison and Beaubien 2010.

31. Emmerich 1984, 160.

32. In lost-wax casting, pathways for the flow of metal and release of gases, called vents and sprues, are incorporated into the mold. When the mold is filled with molten metal these pathways are filled with metal and need to be removed after casting. For a good description and illustrations of the lost-wax technique as it pertains to the Americas, see Fleming 1992, 50–51.

33. Howe 1985.

34. Craddock 2009.

35. For an overview of the causes and occurrences of manganese staining on New World ceramics, see O'Grady 2005.

36. For a thorough description of the use of thermoluminescence dating in the detection of fakes and forgeries, see Craddock 2009, 110–25.

37. Five drilled samples were taken from this urn and sent to Oxford Authentication Ltd. for thermoluminescence dating. All the samples came back with "estimated dates of the last firing between 1,200 and 1,900 years ago." This was consistent with the suggested period of manufacture for the urn, between 400 and 800 CE.

38. Shaplin 1978. Additionally, there are published references for "fake certificates" of known terracotta forgeries, in this case from Africa. See Brent 2001.

39. Ellen Howe, objects conservator at the Metropolitan Museum of Art, brought to my attention the fact that the Chinese forgers have developed a technique for artificially inducing age in ceramics that is indistinguishable from natural aging by the process of thermoluminescence. The technique has been in use for approximately the last ten years, so artifacts in collections prior to that could not have been forged using this technique.

40. The website of the Foundation for the Advancement of Mesoamerican Studies, www.famsi.org, is an excellent resource for studies in ancient American ceramics.

41. Townsend 1998a.

42. X-radiography of the ceramics was done at the Walters Art Museum using a Kimtron Inc. Polaris MC-250 and processed with GE Digital software and scanner. Images taken at 90Kv, 2.0 ma for 45 seconds. The image was enhanced with sharpening filters and contrast adjustments.

43. The author has observed differences in the appearance of clay bodies viewed in x-radiography. The use of organic temper was noted in some Nayarit ceramics; the Jalisco pieces examined all had large radio-dense inclusions and in that way differed from the Lagunillas figures being discussed.

44. Our thanks to Dr. Barry Daly at the University of Maryland Hospital, who performed the CT scans of three West Mexican ceramics in the collection. Initial processing of the images shows very promising results, and though images were not available for this publication, there will be continued research on fabrication techniques for the West Mexican ceramics, in which CT images will be used. A publication will center on the work that focused primarily on ceramic fabrication techniques gleaned from the work done at the Walters and in conjunction with Dr. Daly and his colleagues at the University of Maryland.

45. Important work using XRF analysis to determine the composition and colorants of the slips was conducted by Glenn Gates with assistance from Jessie Arista, contract conservator working on the Bourne Collection. Preliminary results from this investigation were presented at the Research Forum on West Mexican Ceramics held in Baltimore on December 6, 2010.

46. Colburn 2002, 99.

47. Lange 1993, 9.

48. Ibid.

49. Non-destructive Raman analysis was carried out on nine objects (cat. nos. 8, 15, 87–91, checklist nos. 85, and 86) from the Bourne Collection on July 21, 2010, at the Scientific Research and Analysis Laboratory of the Winterthur Museum and Country Estate. The analysis was done by Catherine Matsen, (conservation scientist, Winterthur Museum and Country Estate) with Glenn Gates (conservation scientist, Walters Art Museum) and Jessie Arista (WUD-PAC third-year intern, Walters Art Museum). The nine samples were all identified as jadeite, with albite present in four of the nine objects, diopside in two objects, and omphacite in one object. Though the analyses confirmed the use of the appropriate jadeite minerals, nothing further can be concluded about the authenticity of the objects based on this analysis alone. Raman analysis was done using a Renishaw inVia Raman microscope/dispersive spectrometer calibrated with a silicon crystal. The 514 nm lasers and the 785 nm laser were used, and the spectral range during analysis was 100 to 2000 cm-1, with a spectral resolution of 3 cm-1.

50. West 1963; Gwinnett and Gorelick 1979; Lange 1993, 270.

51. Lange 1993, 270.

52. Scanning electron microscopy imaging has been used to image tool marks and polishing compound residues at a very high magnification. Gwinnett and Gorelick 1979; Gorelick and Gwinnett 1994; Strahan and Fenn 2007.

53. Pasztory 2002, 162.

DIGITAL X-RADIOGRAPHY: Digital x-radiographs were taken of ceramic, metal, jade, and wooden objects to determine construction methods and aid in identification of restorations. Digital x-radiographs were taken using a Polaris (Kimtron, Inc.) x-radiography control system and a Varian x-ray tube using a range of kV and mA (80–160 kV and 2–2.5 mA). The x-ray image was captured on a GE Imaging Technologies phosphor imaging plate for computed tomography. The plate was scanned on a Pegasus Scanner CR50P (GE Inspection Technologies) into Rhythm Acquire (GE Inspection Technologies software). The digital x-ray was viewed using the program Rhythm 2.2 Review (GE Inspection Technologies software).

COMPUTED TOMOGRAPHY: Computed tomography of three West Mexican ceramic objects was conducted at the University of Maryland Medical Center by Dr. Barry Daly (MD, FRCR, Professor of Radiology, Chief of Abdominal Imaging, and Vice Chair for Research, Department of Diagnostic Radiology) and his staff. Computed tomography (CT-scan) employs x-ray technology to provide detailed three-dimensional x-ray images and was used to elucidate methods of original construction and later restorations.

THERMOLUMINESCENCE DATING: Thermoluminescence (TL) analysis is a dating technique applicable to fired ceramic material. Under a red safelight, 100 mg samples were drilled with a straight-edged tungsten carbide bit from selected ceramics. TL analysis establishes the time that has elapsed since the material was last heated, i.e. when it was fired during manufacture. Samples were sent to Oxford Authentication, Ltd., Oxfordshire (www.oxfordauthentication), for analysis.

CARBON-14 DATING: Carbon-14 dating is a dating technique for organic materials based on levels of an unstable carbon isotope, C14. Radiocarbon dating identifies when the raw material, such as wood, stopped growing, i.e., when a tree was cut down. It cannot identify when the artifact was made. Wood samples in the range of 50–300 mg were taken

with a clean chisel or scalpel from selected samples sites and were sent to Rafter GNS Science for analysis (www.rafterradiocarbon.co.nz).

X-RAY FLUORESCENCE ANALYSIS: This non-destructive technique was employed on metal objects (gold, silver, copper alloy), ceramics, and jade objects to study the elements present in the alloys, pigments/surface decoration, and clay bodies. A Bruker AXS ARTAX μXRF spectrometer equipped with a rhodium tube and accompanying software was used at a variety of operating voltages and collection times for both qualitative and quantitative analysis. The data collected and interpreted at the Walters Art Museum by Glenn Gates with assistance from Julie Lauffenburger and Jessica Arista.

CROSS-SECTION MICROSCOPY: This technique was used to determine the stratigraphy of the decorative paint layers. Samples were removed using a #11 scalpel and embedded in WARD's Natural Science BioPlastic® Liquid casting plastic (polyester resin) hardened with WARD's Methyl Ethyl Ketone Peroxide catalyst. Samples were dry polished using MicroMesh® (grades 400–12000), were mounted for viewing with a cover-slip and viewed using a Leitz Wetzlar Ortholux polarized light microscope in reflected light. (10x, 20x, 50x objectives X 10x ocular). A Nikon D40 digital camera was used to capture digital images.

RAMAN SPECTROSCOPY: Non-destructive Raman analysis was carried out on selected jade objects in order to determine their exact mineral composition at the Scientific Research and Analysis Laboratory of the Winterthur Museum and Country Estate on July 21, 2010. The analysis was done by Catherine Matsen, Conservation Scientist (Winterthur Museum and Country Estate) with Glenn Gates (Conservation Scientist, Walters Art Museum) and Jessica Arista (then graduate intern, Walters Art Museum).

Raman analysis was done using a Renishaw inVia Raman microscope/dispersive spectrometer calibrated with a silicon crystal. The 514 nm laser and the 785 nm lasers were used and the spectral range during analysis was 100 to 2000 cm^{-1} with a spectral resolution of 3 cm^{-1}. Qualitative analysis was done using spectral libraries and published articles; the spectral libraries referred to for identification include Robin Clark's library, published in *Spectrochemica Acta*, the Mineral Raman database from the University of Arizona, and the Infrared and Raman Users Group (IRUG) database. Published articles on the Raman analysis of jadeite and nephrite jades were used as references.

FOURIER-TRANSFORM INFRARED SPECTROSCOPY (FT-IR): FT-IR is useful for analyzing materials such as adhesives, binding media, pigments, plastics, and surface coatings. Analysis at the Walters was performed by Glenn Gates on a Bruker Hyperion FT-IR Microscope, attached to a Bruker Tensor spectrometer, in transmission mode. Samples were removed from the objects using a #11 scalpel. Operating parameters for the analysis were a spectral range of 4,000 to 650 cm^{-1} with a spectral resolution of 4 cm^{-1} and a collection time of 100 to 500 scans. The software used with the spectrometer is OPUS; in it, access was provided to the IRUG libraries.

METALLOGRAPHIC CROSS SECTIONS AND SCANNING ELECTRON MICROSCOPY/ENERGY-DISPERSIVE X-RAY SPECTROMETRY (SEM-EDS): Samples taken from metal artifacts were embedded in Buehler EpoxiCure® Epoxy Resin and EpoxiCure® Epoxy Hardener. The resin and hardener were mixed together in a 5:1 ratio and poured into a reusable EPDM (rubber) mounting cup (Buehler), the interior of which had been coated with Aero-Chem Hi-Grade Silicon Spray Lubricant and Release Agent. The metal samples were polished using coarse grinding wheels followed by Micro-Mesh (Micro-Surface Finishing Products, Inc.) grits 3,200 to 12,000, and finished with 0.25 micron grit Buehler diamond polish on a cloth-covered wheel.

The polished cross sections were submitted for examination and analysis using SEM-EDS, to Richard Newman, Head of Scientific Research at the Museum of Fine Arts,

Boston. Line scans, X-ray mapping, and small-area analysis were used to determine overall alloy composition and homogeneity of metal composition, including whether surface depletion or enrichment had taken place. Overall compositions of the metal alloy were determined by taking an average of analyses of several different regions of the exposed area of each metal cross section.

Samples were examined in a JOEL JSM-6460LV scanning electron microscope with an attached Oxford Instruments INCA 'x-Sight' energy-dispersive x-ray spectrometer (EDS) with 133 eV resolution. Samples were examined as sent, without carbon coating, in low-vacuum mode at a chamber pressure of 35 pascals. The SEM was operated at 20kV with a beam current of about 1 nanoamp. NBS standard microprobe reference materials were used for quantitative analyses (Au-Ag system, SRM 481; and Au-Cu system, SRM 482). In the SEM, samples were examined by back-scattered electron imaging. For quantitative analysis, counting times for each were 100 seconds. Maps were acquired over 3,600 seconds and point-by-point scans shown for each sample were acquired for ten seconds at each point (description from analytical report received from Richard Newman, Museum of Fine Arts, Boston).

Head from Female Figure, checklist no. 9

CHECKLIST

1. STANDING FIGURE

Olmec style, Mexico
Jadeite (?)
21.7 × 6.4 × 4.5 cm
TL.2009.20.124

2. STANDING FIGURE

Olmec style, Mexico
Jadeite (?)
15.1 × 5.4 × 4.8 cm
TL.2009.20.125

3. MASK

Olmec style, Mexico

Jadeite (?), red pigment

13 × 10.3 × 3.9 cm

TL.2009.20.129

4. EFFIGY CELT

Olmec style, Mexico

Jadeite (?)

9.8 × 4.5 × 2.8 cm

TL.2009.20.119

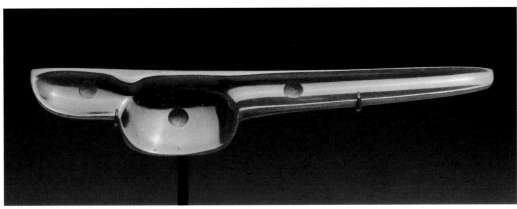

5. PECTORAL (RITUAL OBJECT)

Olmec style, Mexico

Jadeite (?)

16 × 3.5 × 1 cm

TL.2009.20.229

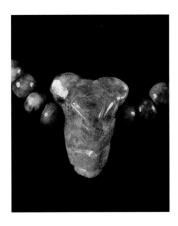

6. SPHERICAL BEADS AND CANINE (?) EFFIGY BEAD

Olmec, Mexico

Early Formative Period,

1200–900 BCE

Jadeite (?)

Pendant: 4.2 × 3.4 × 1.9 cm;

necklace: length 60.6 cm

TL.2009.20.237

7. FOREARM EFFIGY PENDANT

Olmec style, Mexico

Jadeite (?)

14.4 × 4.4 × 4.8 cm

TL.2009.20.276

8. TRIPOD DISH

Olmec, Guerrero, Mexico (?)

Middle Formative Period,

900–600 BCE

Burnished earthenware

Height 8.9 cm, diameter 12.3 cm

TL.2009.20.220

9. HEAD FROM FEMALE FIGURE

Tlapacoya (?), Morelos or

Puebla, Mexico (?)

Early Formative Period,

1200–900 BCE

Burnished earthenware, slip paint

28.7 × 17. 8 × 13.5 cm

TL.2009.20.183

10. EFFIGY CELT

Mezcala style, Guerrero, Mexico
Stone
9.7 × 3.8 × 2.5 cm
TL.2009.20.157

11. EFFIGY CELT

Mezcala style, Guerrero, Mexico
Stone
20.3 × 7.6 × 5.1 cm
TL.2009.20.159

12. HUMAN EFFIGY

Mezcala style, Guerrero, Mexico
Stone
6.1 × 3.3 × 3 cm
TL.2009.20.299

13. MASK

Chontal style, Guerrero, Mexico
Stone
18.6 × 10.9 × 7.3 cm
TL.2009.20.127

14. SQUASH-SHAPED VESSEL

Colima, Mexico
Late Formative to Early Classic
Periods, 200 BCE–300 CE
Earthenware, burnished slip
25.2 × 35.8 × 35.4 cm
TL.2009.20.213

15. DWARF-SHAMAN EFFIGY VESSEL

Colima, Mexico

Comala phase, 100 BCE–300 CE (?)

Earthenware, burnished light brown and red slip, with incising

35 × 39.1 × 20.9 cm

2009.20.54

16. SHAMAN EFFIGY VESSEL

Colima, Mexico

Comala phase, 100 BCE–300 CE

Earthenware, burnished light brown and red slip paint, with incising

36.2 × 24.5 × 17.7 cm

TL.2009.20.289

17. SHAMAN (?) EFFIGY FIGURE

Colima style, Mexico

Earthenware, burnished slip (red)

31.5 × 23.1 × 16.5 cm

TL.2009.20.290

18. SEATED FEMALE EFFIGY VESSEL WITH TALL SPOUT

Colima, Mexico

Late Formative to Early Classic Periods, 200 BCE–300 CE

Burnished earthenware

29.6 × 20.9 × 25.8 cm

TL.2009.20.181

19. SEATED SHAMAN (?) EFFIGY VESSEL

Colima, Mexico

Late Formative to Early Classic Periods, 200 BCE–300 CE

Earthenware, burnished slip

28.9 × 22.7 × 28.6 cm

TL.2009.20.167

20. FIGURE CARRYING JARS EFFIGY

Colima, Mexico

Late Formative to Early Classic
Periods, 200 BCE–300 CE

Burnished earthenware

24.6 × 19.1 × 21.3 cm

TL.2009.20.164

21. SEATED MALE EFFIGY VESSEL

Colima, Mexico

Classic Period, 100–900 CE

Earthenware, burnished slip

22.1 × 26.9 × 22.9 cm

TL.2009.20.187

22. DWARF EFFIGY (HEAD FRAGMENT)

Colima, Mexico

Comala phase, 100 BCE–300 CE

Earthenware, incising

16.7 × 15.9 × 17.3 cm

TL.2009.20.107

23. HUMAN EFFIGY FLUTE

Colima, Mexico

Late Formative to Early Classic
Periods, 200 BCE–300 CE

Earthenware, post-fire paint (green)

15.7 × 8.5 × 6.7 cm

TL.2009.20.296

24. SEATED MALE EFFIGY VESSEL

Colima, Mexico

Late Formative to Early Classic
Periods, 200 BCE–300 CE

Burnished earthenware

34.1 × 19.6 × 18.8 cm

TL.2009.20.166

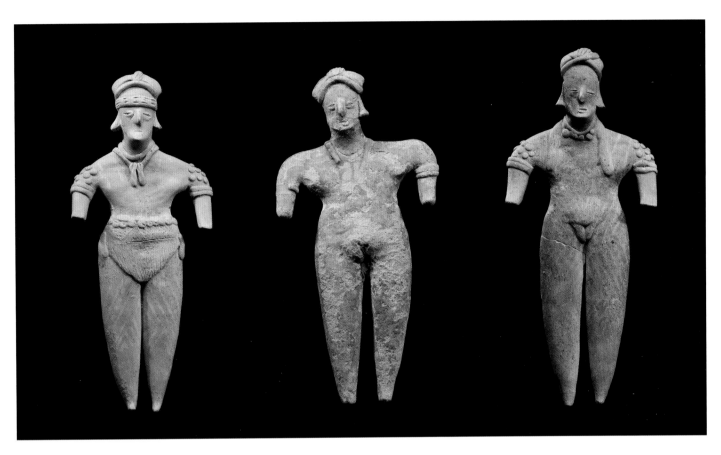

25. THREE STANDING FEMALE FIGURES AND ONE SEATED MALE

Colima, Mexico
Late Formative to Early Classic Periods, 300 BCE–200 CE
2009.20.60.1 (above, left): Earthenware, slip paint; 30.5 × 13.1 × 4.5 cm
2009.20.60.2 (above, center): Earthenware; 27.9 × 14.2 × 4.4 cm
2009.20.60.3 (above, right): Earthenware, slip paint; 35.8 × 15.6 × 5.3 cm
2009.20.60.4 (left): Earthenware, slip paint; 24.9 × 20.7 × 11.2 cm

26. FEMALE FIGURINE

Colima, Mexico
Late Formative to Early Classic
Periods, 300 BCE–200 CE
Earthenware
17.3 × 8.6 × 2.8 cm
TL.2009.20.173

27. FEMALE FIGURINE

Colima, Mexico
Late Formative to Early Classic
Periods, 300 BCE–200 CE
Earthenware, slip paint
18.8 × 9.1 × 2.8 cm
TL.2009.20.174

28. PREGNANT
FEMALE FIGURE

Colima, Mexico

300 BCE–200 CE

Earthenware, incising

16.5 × 7.7 × 4.1 cm

TL.2009.20.136

29. FEMALE FIGURE

Colima, Atlan, West Mexico
Late Formative to Early Classic
Periods, 300 BCE–200 CE
Earthenware, incising
16.1 × 4.8 × 4.7 cm
TL.2009.20.122

30. SEATED FEMALE (?) FIGURE

Colima, Mexico
Late Formative to Early Classic
Periods, 300 BCE–200 CE
Earthenware
10 × 6.6 × 5.4 cm
TL.2009.20.154

31. SEATED MALE FIGURE WITH TALL VESSEL

Colima-Nayarit, Colima or
Nayarit, Mexico (?)
Late Formative to Early Classic
Periods, 300 BCE–200 CE
Earthenware
43.8 × 22.9 × 14.5 cm
TL.2009.20.287.1

32. THREE KNIFE/AXE FORMS

Colima-Nayarit, Colima or
Nayarit, Mexico (?)
Late Formative to Early Classic
Periods, 300 BCE–200 CE
Obsidian (3), chert (2, 4)
Largest (287.3): 11.4 × 4.5 × 1.3 cm
TL.2009.20.287.2–4
Found with checklist no. 31

33. SEATED FIGURE

Colima-Nayarit, Colima or
Nayarit, Mexico (?)
Late Formative to Early Classic
Periods, 300 BCE–200 CE
Earthenware
8.4 × 5.6 × 5 cm
TL.2009.20.155

34. KNEELING FEMALE FIGURE

Nayarit, Mexico
Late Formative to Early Classic
Periods, 300 BCE–200 CE
Earthenware, white slip over slip
paint in black and red
27.4 × 16.2 × 13.5 cm
2009.20.14

35. SEATED MALE FIGURE

Nayarit, Mexico
Late Formative to Early Classic
Periods, 300 BCE–200 CE (?)
Earthenware, slip paint, with incising
58 × 26.9 × 26.8 cm
TL.2009.20.163

36. STANDING FEMALE FIGURE

Nayarit, Mexico
Late Formative to Early Classic
Periods, 300 BCE–200 CE (?)
Earthenware, slip paint
61.2 × 26 × 16.1 cm
2009.20.12

37. SEATED FEMALE FIGURE

Nayarit, Mexico
Late Formative to Early Classic
Periods, 300 BCE–200 CE
Earthenware, slip paint
55.4 × 37.4 × 31.4 cm
2009.20.40

38. SEATED MALE FIGURE

Nayarit, Mexico
Late Formative to Early Classic
Periods, 300 BCE–200 CE
Earthenware, slip paint
60.4 × 36.5 × 29.7 cm
2009.20.42

39. SEATED FIGURE WITH DOG

Nayarit, Mexico
Late Formative to Early Classic
Periods, 300 BCE–200 CE
Earthenware, slip paint
11.7 × 6.5 × 6 cm
TL.2009.20.112

40. SEATED MALE (?) FIGURE

Jalisco, Mexico
Late Formative to Early Classic
Periods, 300 BCE–200 CE
Earthenware, slip paint, incising
18.4 × 12 × 7.8 cm
TL.2009.20.103

41. SEATED FIGURE

Jalisco, Mexico
Late Formative to Early Classic
Periods, 300 BCE–200 CE (?)
Burnished earthenware
18.9 × 15.4 × 12.5 cm
TL.2009.20.143

42. SEATED MALE SHAMAN FIGURE

Jalisco, Mexico
Late Formative to Early Classic
Periods, 300 BCE–200 CE (?)
Burnished earthenware
16.5 × 16.8 × 12.9 cm
TL.2009.20.144

43. SEATED MALE FIGURE

El Arenal, Jalisco, Mexico
Late Formative to Early Classic
Periods, 100 BCE–200 CE
Earthenware, slip paint
56.4 × 36.7 × 28 cm
2009.20.58

44. HUMAN EFFIGY FLUTE

Jalisco style, Jalisco, Mexico
Burnished earthenware
35.6 × 7.4 × 5.7 cm
TL.2009.20.132

45. PROCESSIONAL SCENE (MEN CARRYING PULQUE JARS)

Jalisco style, Jalisco, Mexico

Earthenware, slip paint (red)

18.7 × 31 × 20.8 cm

TL.2009.20.291

46. TOBACCO PIPE

Michoacan, Mexico

Late Formative to Classic Periods, 300 BCE–800 CE

Burnished earthenware

8.2 × 18.8 × 5.1 cm

TL.2009.20.131

47. FEMALE FIGURE

Chupícuaro, Guanajuato, Mexico

Late Formative to Early Classic Periods, 300 BCE–100 CE

Earthenware, slip paint

10.1 × 5.4 × 3 cm

TL.2009.20.152

48. FEMALE FIGURE

Chupícuaro, Guanajuato, Mexico

Late Formative to Early Classic Periods, 300 BCE–100 CE

Earthenware, slip paint

9.5 × 5 × 2.8 cm

TL.2009.20.153

49. TRIPOD DISH

Chupícuaro, Guanajuato, Mexico
Late Formative to Early Classic
Periods, 300 BCE–100 CE
Burnished earthenware
8.9 × 18.5 × 17 cm
TL.2009.20.146

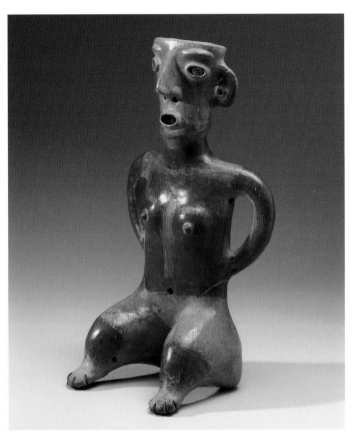

50. SEATED
FEMALE FIGURE

Zacatecas, Jalisco-Zacatecas
border region, Mexico
Late Formative to Early Classic
Periods, 100–300 CE
Earthenware, slip paint
33 × 18.2 × 12.9 cm
TL.2009.20.195

51. FEMALE PERFORMER
HOLDING DRUM AND
STRIKER OR RATTLE

Zacatecas style, Jalisco-Zacatecas
border region, Mexico
Earthenware (paint)
8.6 × 3.3 × 2.5 cm
TL.2009.20.225

52. SEATED FEMALE
HOLDING CHILD

Zacatecas, Jalisco-Zacatecas
border region, Mexico
Late Formative to Early Classic
Periods, 300 BCE–200 CE
Earthenware, paint
10.6 × 5.1 × 4. 5 cm
TL.2009.20.266

53. STANDING FIGURE

Zacatecas, Jalisco-Zacatecas
border region, Mexico
Late Formative to Early Classic
Periods, 300 BCE–200 CE
Earthenware, paint
16.1 × 7.1 × 3.5 cm
TL.2009.20.267

54. SEVEN SMALL FIGURINES

Zacatecas, Jalisco-Zacatecas
border region, Mexico
Late Formative to Early Classic Periods, 300 BCE–200 CE
Earthenware
TL.2009.20.268.1: 2.3 × 1.1 × 0.8 cm
TL.2009.20.268.2: 2.9 × 1.6 × 1 cm
TL.2009.20.268.3: 4.9 × 1.6 × 1 cm
TL.2009.20.268.4: 5.5 × 2.3 × 1.3 cm
TL.2009.20.268.5: 4.3 × 1.8 × 1.1 cm
TL.2009.20.268.6: 3.8 × 1.6 × 1 cm
TL.2009.20.268.7: 3 × 2 × 1.4 cm

55. MALE FIGURE

Olmec-early Teotihuacan style,
central Mexico (?)
Green stone
34.2 × 12.8 × 7.4 cm
TL.2009.20.300

56. MALE FIGURE

Teotihuacan style, Teotihuacan,
Mexico
Green stone
14.5 × 5. 6 × 1.8 cm
TL.2009.20.114

57. MASK

Teotihuacan style, Teotihuacan,
Mexico
Stone
19.1 × 18.7 × 9.2 cm
TL.2009.20.216

58. TRIPOD VESSEL

Zapotec, Oaxaca, Mexico
Middle Classic Period, 300–700 CE
Earthenware
Height 10 cm, diameter 9.8 cm
TL.2009.20.93

59. EFFIGY URN

Monte Albán style, Oaxaca, Mexico
Earthenware, post-fire pigment (red)
21.9 × 14.7 × 13 cm
TL.2009.20.247

60. INCENSE BURNER LID

Mixteca-Puebla style, Oaxaca or
Puebla, Mexico (?)
Earthenware, slip paint
52.4 × 65 × 41 cm
2009.20.19

61. XOCHIPILI (?) EFFIGY

Mixteca-Puebla, Puebla or
Oaxaca, Mexico (?)
Postclassic Period, 1200–1521 CE
Earthenware, paint
74.8 × 47 × 48.4 cm
TL.2009.20.197

62. "XANTIL" INCENSE BURNER EFFIGY LID

Mixteca-Puebla, Puebla or
Oaxaca, Mexico (?)
Postclassic Period, 1200–1521 CE
Earthenware, post-fire paint
32.4 × 25.4 × 12.7 cm
TL.2009.20.188

63. LABRET

Mixteca-Puebla style, Oaxaca or
Puebla, Mexico (?)
Obsidian, traces of red pigment
5.9 × 1.9 × 2.9 cm
TL.2009.20.249

64. XIUHTECUHTLI (?) EFFIGY INCENSE BURNER

Toltec or Aztec style,
central Mexico
Stone, traces of red pigment
26.4 × 12.6 × 12.6 cm
TL.2009.20.200

65. PECTORAL

Mixtec style, Mexico
Gold alloy
9.7 × 6.3 × 1.7 cm
TL.2009.20.301

66. RATTLESNAKE EFFIGY

Aztec style, Mexico

Stone

34.7 × 34.4 × 35.2 cm

TL.2009.20.191

67. MANTA RAY EFFIGY FIGURE

Kino Viejo-Seri, Baja California or Sonora, Mexico (?)

1550–1800 CE

Earthenware, with incising

10.2 × 3.8 × 1.8 cm

TL.2009.20.252

68. XIPE TOTEC IMPERSONATOR

Remojadas, Veracruz, Mexico

Late Classic Period, 600–900 CE

Earthenware, black paint

54.3 × 27.3 × 19.7 cm

2009.20.11

69. BATTERED WARRIOR (?) FIGURE

Remojadas, Veracruz, Mexico

Late Classic Period, 600–900 CE

Earthenware, black paint

48.3 × 32.9 × 24.6 cm

2009.20.44

70. RITUAL PERFORMER

Remojadas or Nopiloa, southern
Veracruz, Mexico
Late Classic Period, 600–800 CE
Earthenware
40.8 × 25.6 × 13.4 cm
2009.20.43

71. RITUAL PERFORMER

Remojadas or Nopiloa, southern
Veracruz, Mexico
Late Classic Period, 600–800 CE
Earthenware
40.4 × 27.6 × 11.3 cm
2009.20.48

72. HEAD FROM RITUAL
PERFORMER FIGURE

Remojadas or Nopiloa, southern
Veracruz, Mexico
Late Classic Period, 600–800 CE
Earthenware
12.7 × 14 × 10.2 cm
TL.2009.20.184

73. TRIPOD VESSEL

Maya, Ulùa Valley in Honduras
Late Classic Period, 550–850 CE
Earthenware, slip paint
Height 24.7 cm, diameter 20.4 cm
2009.20.34

74. VESSEL

Maya, Guatemala or Mexico (?)
Late Classic Period, 550–850 CE
Burnished earthenware, traces
of stucco and post-fire paint
(red and green)
Height 11.1 cm, diameter 13.7 cm
TL.2009.20.294

75. SEATED MALE FIGURE

Maya, Jaina Island (?) in Campeche,
Mexico
Late Classic Period, 550–850 CE
Earthenware, post-fire paint (red)
26.2 × 16.1 × 13.8 cm
2009.20.31

76. SEATED MALE FIGURE

Maya, Jaina Island in Campeche,
Mexico
Late Classic Period, 550–850 CE
Earthenware, post-fire paint
12.8 × 6.3 × 6.9 cm
TL.2009.20.113

77. PROFILE FACE
(FRAGMENT)

Maya-Olmec, Mexico or
Guatemala (?)
Late Preclassic Period,
300 BCE–250 CE
Stone
18.1 × 9.3 × 2.8 cm
TL.2009.20.233

78. FIGURINE HEAD

Maya, Jonuta, Tabasco, Mexico
Late Preclassic Period,
300 BCE–250 CE
Earthenware
9.2 × 2.6 × 5 cm
TL.2009.20.295

79. HUMAN HEAD AND ANIMAL EFFIGY BEADS

Maya, San Cristobal de las
Casas, Mexico (?)
Postclassic Period, 850–1521 CE
Earthenware
Largest (251.4): 2.3 × 5.1 × 1 cm
TL.2009.20.251.1–7

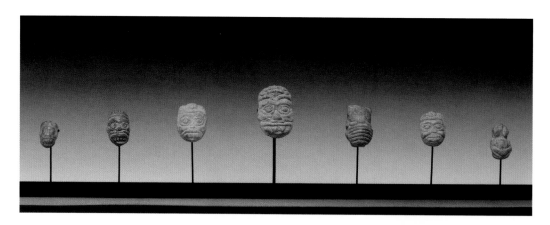

80. INCENSE BURNER

Maya, Escuintla, Guatemala
350–550 CE
Earthenware, post-fire paint
103.8 × 46.7 × 38 cm
2009.20.57
The object was sampled in three
areas for thermoluminescence dating;
all samples were reported to be last
fired 1,100–1,800 years ago, consistent with the proposed date range
of manufacture. The analysis was
performed by Oxford Authentication Ltd., Oxfordshire, England.

81. TUBULAR BEAD

Maya, Maya Lowlands, Mexico,
Guatemala, Belize or Honduras
Classic Period, 250–850 CE
Green stone
31.5 × 3.1 × 2.6 cm
TL.2009.20.258

82. NECKLACE

Maya (?), Mexico, Guatemala,
Belize, or Honduras
Classic to Postclassic Periods,
250–1521 CE
Shell
Pendant: 80.4 × 11.5 × 1.5 cm; neck-
lace: length 59.5 cm
TL.2009.20.297

83. NECKLACE
WITH PENDANTS

Maya, Maya Lowlands, Mexico,
Guatemala, Belize, or Honduras
Late Preclassic to Classic Periods,
300 BCE–850 CE
Green stone
Pendants: length 2.6–4.2 cm;
necklace: length 82 cm
TL.2009.20.271

84. SCEPTER (?)

Maya-Toltec, Yucatan or
Campeche, Mexico (?)
Postclassic Period, 850–1521 CE
Green stone
15.9 × 1.9 × 1.6 cm
TL.2009.20.240

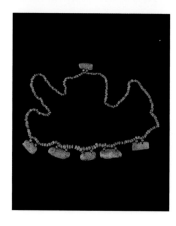

85. MASK

Maya style, Guatemala

Jadeite

Mask: 7.9 × 8.9 × 2.6 cm

TL.2009.20.298

86. MASK WITH PENDANT BEADS

Maya style, Guatemala

Jadeite

14.8 × 14.7 × 4.9 cm

TL.2009.20.123.1–11

87. PENDANT

Maya style, Mexico or Guatemala (?)

Jadeite (?)

7.7 × 6.6 × 2.2 cm

TL.2009.20.130

88. ECCENTRIC

Maya style, Guatemala or Honduras (?)

Flint

12.2 × 4.8 × 0.8 cm

TL.2009.20.224

89. ECCENTRIC

Maya style, Guatemala

Flint

29 × 14 × 1.3 cm

TL.2009.20.235

90. HACHA

Maya, Guatemala

Classic Period, 250–850 CE (?)

Stone

22.9 × 30 × 4.9 cm

TL.2009.20.203

91. BELL PENDANTS

Maya, Yucatan, Mexico

Postclassic Period, 850–1521 CE

Copper alloy

TL.2009.20.147.1: length 29.5 cm

TL.2009.20.147.2–3: 0.2–0.7 cm

92. WARRIOR FIGURE

Atlantic Watershed style,
Guapiles, Costa Rica

Volcanic stone

95.6 × 62.9 × 30.6 cm

2009.20.25

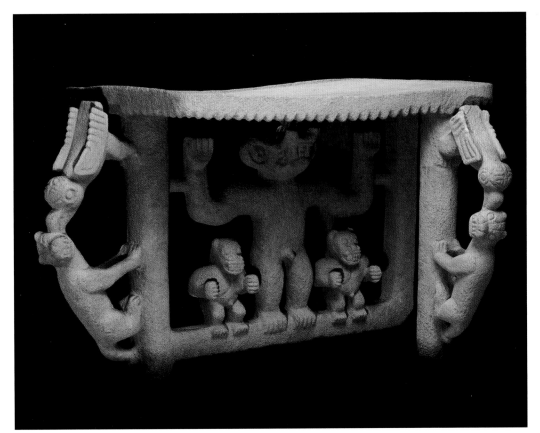

93. CEREMONIAL METATE

Atlantic Watershed style,
Costa Rica
Volcanic stone
56 × 94.4 × 78 cm
2009.20.24

94. METATE

Atlantic Watershed, Costa Rica
Late Period V–Period VI,
900–1500 CE
Stone
23.5 × 130 × 42.5 cm
TL.2009.20.170

95. HUMAN EFFIGY
OCARINA

Atlantic Watershed, Costa Rica
Period IV, 200–500 CE
Earthenware, slip paint
13.8 × 7.9 × 6.2 cm
TL.2009.20.92

96. TRIPOD VESSEL

Atlantic Watershed, Costa Rica

Late Period IV–Early Period V,

300–700 CE

Earthenware, with burnishing at lip

18.1 × 18.2 × 15.9 cm

TL.2009.20.210

97. TRIPOD VESSEL

Guanacaste-Nicoya zone,

Costa Rica

Late Period IV, 300–500 CE

Earthenware, burnished slip paint,

with incising

16.5 × 27.9 × 24.8 cm

TL.2009.20.189

98. TRIPOD VESSEL

Diquís, Costa Rica
Period VI, 1000–1500 CE
Earthenware
12.7 × 11 × 11 cm
TL.2009.20.94

99. TRIPOD VESSEL

Guanacaste-Nicoya, Costa Rica
Late Period V–Early Period VI,
800–1200 CE
Earthenware, slip paint
Height 9.5 cm, diameter 18.2 cm
TL.2009.20.151

100. SHAMAN EFFIGY VESSEL

Guanacaste-Nicoya, Costa Rica
Late Period VI, 1000–1350 CE
Earthenware, white slip overall,
slip paint
30.5 × 24.1 × 24.4 cm
2009.20.56

101. CROCODILE EFFIGY PENDANT

Atlantic Watershed style,
Costa Rica
Green stone
15.7 × 2.9 × 1.3 cm
TL.2009.20.273

102. JAGUAR EFFIGY MACE HEAD

Guanacaste-Nicoya style,
Costa Rica
Green stone
6 × 7.3 × 9.4 cm
TL.2009.20.106

103. SERPENT EFFIGY MACE HEAD

Guanacaste-Nicoya style,
Costa Rica
Green stone
7 × 11.6 × 5.2 cm
TL.2009.20.108

104. "AXE GOD" PENDANT

Central Pacific area style,
Costa Rica
Jadeite (?)
19 × 5.9 × 1.2 cm
TL.2009.20.118

105. AVIAN "AXE GOD" PENDANT

Guanacaste-Nicoya style,
Costa Rica
Jadeite (?)
18.7 × 7.4 × 3.5 cm
TL.2009.20.256

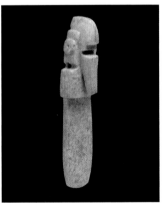

106. AVIAN "AXE GOD" PENDANT

Guanacaste-Nicoya style,
Costa Rica
Jadeite (?)
15.1 × 3.4 × 2.9 cm
TL.2009.20.257

107. HUMAN FACE PENDANT

Guanacaste-Nicoya, Costa Rica
Period IV, 500 BCE–500 CE
Jadeite (?)
3.5 × 4 × 1.4 cm
TL.2009.20.223

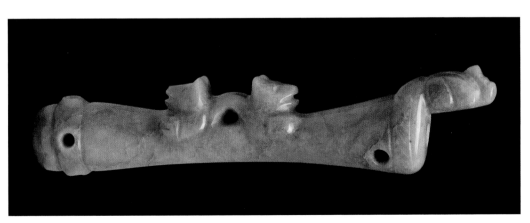

108. TUBULAR PENDANT BEAD

Guanacaste-Nicoya (?), Costa Rica
Period IV, 1–500 CE (?)
Jadeite (?)
3.8 × 17.3 × 2.6 cm
TL.2009.20.238

109. HUMAN EFFIGY PENDANT

Coclé style, Panama

Cast gold alloy

5.4 × 3.9 × 1.4 cm

TL.2009.20.72

Qualitative x-ray fluorescence analysis identified the presence of gold, copper and silver.

110. FROG EFFIGY PENDANT

Coclé, Panama

700–1500 CE

Cast gold alloy

1.7 × 4.4 × 2.4 cm

TL.2009.20.77

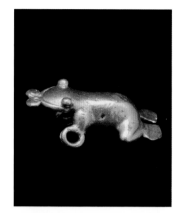

111. CROCODILE EFFIGY LIME DIPPER

Coclé style, Panama

Cast gold alloy

10.6 × 5.4 × 1.8 cm

TL.2009.20.84

Qualitative x-ray fluorescence analysis identified the presence of gold and copper; no silver was detected.

112. AVIAN PENDANT

Veraguas style, Veraguas, Panama

Cast gold alloy

8.8 × 11.1 × 2.7 cm

TL.2009.20.82

Qualitative x-ray fluorescence analysis identified the presence of gold, copper, and silver.

113. SHAMAN EFFIGY PENDANT

International style, Panama or Colombia (?)

Cast gold alloy

6.9 × 5 × 1.1 cm

TL.2009.20.83

Qualitative x-ray fluorescence analysis identified the presence of gold, copper, and silver, with silver content in keeping with elevated levels of other Colombian examples.

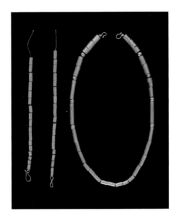

114. TUBULAR BEAD NECKLACE

Coclé, Panama

700–1550 CE

Gold alloy

TL.2009.20.88.1: length 50.7 cm

TL.2009.20.88.2a: length 16.3 cm

TL.2009.20.88.2b: length 18.7 cm

115. EFFIGY "COLLAR"

Taino style, Dominican Republic or Puerto Rico (?)

Stone

46.7 × 11.4 × 44.5 cm

TL.2009.20.190

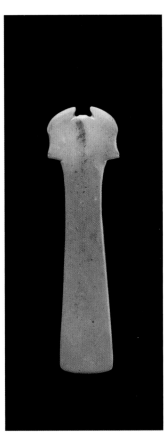

116. RITUAL OBJECT (SCEPTER?)

Tairona, Sierra Nevada de Santa Marta, Colombia

900–1600 CE

Jadeite (?)

53 × 6.6 × 1.6 cm

TL.2009.20.140

117. RITUAL OBJECT (SCEPTER?)

Tairona, Sierra Nevada de Santa Marta, Colombia

900–1600 CE

Stone

25.4 × 6.9 × 1.3 cm

TL.2009.20.142

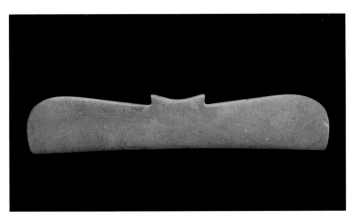

118. ORNAMENT

Tairona, Sierra Nevada de Santa Marta, Colombia

900–1600 CE

Jadeite (?)

5.6 × 31 × 1.1 cm

TL.2009.20.141

119. HUMAN EFFIGY PENDANT

Zenú (Sinú)-Darién style, northwestern Colombia

Cast gold alloy

12.8 × 7 × 2.8 cm

2009.20.67

Qualitative x-ray fluorescence analysis identified the presence of gold, copper, and silver.

120. HUMAN EFFIGY PENDANT

Zenú (Sinú)-Darién style, northwestern Colombia

Gold alloy

14.7 × 8.2 × 2.6 cm

2009.20.68

121. FROG EFFIGY PENDANT

Zenú (Sinú)-Darién, northwestern Colombia

900–1550 CE

Gold alloy

1.3 × 1.9 × 1.9 cm

TL.2009.20.78

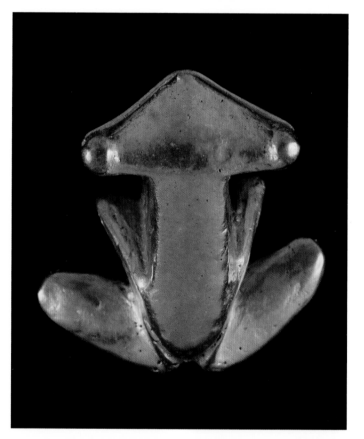

122. SEATED MALE FIGURE

Quimbaya (Caldas complex), Middle Cauca River Valley, Colombia

1200–1400 CE

Earthenware

34.2 × 27.6 × 12 cm

TL.2009.20.283

123. FEMALE EFFIGY FIGURE

Quimbaya (?) style, El Bolo (?), Middle Cauca River Valley, Colombia

Gold

11.6 × 5.3 × 3.3 cm

TL.2009.20.87

Qualitative x-ray fluorescence analysis indicates pure gold. Copper may be there as a trace impurity.

124. NOSE ORNAMENT

Calima style, Cauca River Valley, Colombia
Gold alloy
19.9 × 5.2 × 0.1 cm
2009.20.69
Scanning electron microscopy/energy-dispersive x-ray spectrometry (SEM-EDS) analysis of a cross section determined the bulk alloy composition to be Au 72.6% (0.2), Ag 17.3% (0.5) and Cu 10% (0.4). Percentages reported as normalized weight percent averages with standard deviation. X-ray mapping shows no compositional variation across sample.

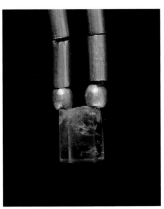

125. PECTORAL

Calima style, Yotoco, Colombia
Gold alloy
17 × 20.2 × 1.8 cm
2009.20.70

126. TUBULAR BEAD NECKLACE AND EMERALD PENDANT

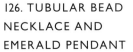

Quimbaya (?), Middle Cauca River Valley, Colombia
100 BCE–1000 CE
Gold alloy, emerald
Pendant: 1.4 × 1.2 × 0.9 cm; necklace: length 53.5 cm
TL.2009.20.75
Qualitative x-ray fluorescence analysis identified the presence of copper and zinc with a surface application of gold.

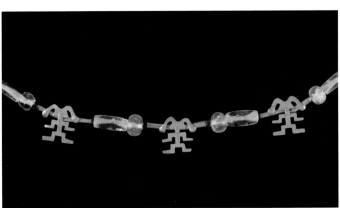

127. ROCK CRYSTAL BEADS AND GOLD PENDANTS NECKLACE

Tolima, Upper Cauca River Valley, Colombia
900–1600 CE
Gold alloy, rock crystal
Length 68.2 cm
TL.2009.20.76

128. BOWL

Nariño, southern Colombia or northern Ecuador
1250–1500 CE
Earthenware, slip paint
Height 9.1 cm, diameter 19.3 cm
TL.2009.20.281

129. SUN DISC WITH CIRCULAR NOSE ORNAMENT

Nariño, El Angel, Ecuador
600–1500 CE
Copper alloy
17 × 17.8 × 1.5 cm
TL.2009.20.100

130. SPHERICAL VESSEL

Carchí, Ecuador

750–1250 CE

Earthenware, negative slip paint

Height 39.7 cm, diameter 41.2 cm

TL.2009.20.150

131. ZOOMORPH EFFIGY

Chorrera, Valdivia, or
Chorrera Ecuador

1200–300 BCE (?)

Green stone

6.8 × 13.9 × 4.4 cm

TL.2009.20.120

132. HUMAN FIGURE
EFFIGY

Valdivia style, coastal Ecuador

Stone

37.1 × 11.2 × 2.9 cm

TL.2009.20.128

133. HUMAN HEAD EFFIGY

Valdivia style, coastal Ecuador

Stone

24.1 × 37.3 × 3.5 cm

TL.2009.20.202

134. SEATED FIGURE
HOLDING A BOX

Jama-Coaque, Ecuador
300 BCE–600 CE
Earthenware, post-fire paint
12.2 × 11.6 × 9.7 cm
TL.2009.20.104

135. FEMALE EFFIGY
FIGURE

Jama-Coaque, Ecuador

300 BCE–600 CE

Partially burnished earthenware,

post-fire paint, with incising

41.4 × 22.1 × 14.61 cm

TL.2009.20.186

136. MONKEY-SHAMAN (?)
EFFIGY FIGURE

Manteño, Manabi, Ecuador

600–1500 CE

Partially burnished earthenware,

post-fire paint (red)

29.9 × 18.8 × 20.6 cm

TL.2009.20.179

137. STIRRUP-SPOUT
BOTTLE

Tembladera, North Coast, Peru

600–200 BCE

Burnished earthenware

Height 24.2 cm, diameter 17. 8 cm

TL.2009.20.96

138. MASK ORNAMENT

Moche, North Coast, Peru
100–600 CE
Copper alloy, shell
21.9 × 28 × 7.5 cm
2009.20.3

139. BELT RATTLE WITH BELLS

Moche style, North Coast, Peru
Gold alloy, turquoise, and *spondylus* shell
9.8 × 18.1 × 2.6 cm
TL.2009.20.66
Scanning electron microscopy/ energy-dispersive x-ray spectrometry (SEM-EDS) analysis of a cross section determined the bulk alloy composition to be Au 86.6% (0.4), Ag 5% (0.3) and Cu 8.4% (0.2). Percentages reported as normalized weight percent averages with standard deviation. X-ray mapping shows no significant compositional variation across sample.

140. PREGNANT WOMAN EFFIGY BOTTLE

Moche, North Coast, Peru
100–600 CE
Earthenware, slip paint
8.9 × 4.6 × 6.8 cm
TL.2009.20.116

141. PREGNANT WOMAN EFFIGY BOTTLE

Moche, North Coast, Peru
Phases III–IV, 300–600 CE
Earthenware, slip paint
9.5 × 4.8 × 6.6 cm
TL.2009.20.115

142. WARRIOR EFFIGY

Moche style, North Coast, Peru

Wood, shell, copper alloy

29.2 × 17.7 × 15 cm

TL.2009.20.242

Radiocarbon dating of a wood sample from the head (reflecting the approximate time when the tree rings were growing) dates the wood, at a 95% confidence level, to an interval between 1306–1364 CE and 1385–1409 CE. While some iconographic elements are consistent with Moche art, others are not. Together, the C-14 and iconographic data suggest that the piece—in its current state— postdates Moche culture by at least 700 years.

143. STIRRUP-SPOUT BOTTLE

Nasca, South Coast, Peru

200–500 CE

Earthenware, slip paint

Height 19.3 cm, diameter 7.9 cm

TL.2009.20.109

144. NECKLACE

Sicán (Lambayeque) style, Piura region, North Coast, Peru

Gold alloy

Pendant: 4.5 × 5 × 1 cm; necklace: length 85.5 cm

TL.2009.20.85

145. ADORNMENT

Sicán (Lambayeque) style, North
Coast, Peru
Gilded brass
4.2 × 6.9 × 0.4 cm
TL.2009.20.79
Qualitative x-ray fluorescence analysis
identified the presence of copper and
zinc with a surface application of gold.

146. ADORNMENT

Sicán (Lambayeque) style, North
Coast, Peru
Gilded brass
4.5 × 7.1 × 0.4 cm
TL.2009.20.80
Qualitative x-ray fluorescence analysis
identified the presence of copper and
zinc with a surface application of gold.

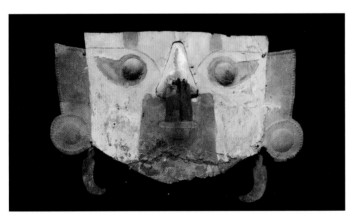

147. FUNERARY MASK

Sicán (Lambayeque), North
Coast, Peru
1000–1200 CE
Copper alloy
23 × 35.6 × 4.5 cm
TL.2009.20.292

148. FUNERARY MASK

Sicán-Chimú style, North
Coast, Peru
Gold alloy
31 × 44.6 × 3.5 cm
2009.20.17
Composed of a single sheet of gold
with attached pendants. SEM-EDS
analysis of a cross section determined the bulk alloy composition to
be Au 65.1% (0.2), Ag 34.7% (0.3)
and Cu 0.2% (0.1). X-ray mapping
shows only very minor variation in
composition of the alloy throughout
with a slight increase in the level of
silver at the surface in one area.

149. COLLAR PECTORAL

Sicán-Chimú style, North
Coast, Peru
Silver alloy
14 × 22.7 × 0.1 cm
TL.2009.20.265
Qualitative x-ray fluorescence
analysis identified the presence of
silver and copper.

150. CEREMONIAL KNIFE (TUMI)

Sicán-Chimú style, North
Coast, Peru
Silver alloy
20.9 × 6.8 × 1.5 cm
TL.2009.20.260
Top portion constructed of two
sheets of hammered silver crimped
together along edges; bottom
section cast and further embellished. The two are joined by an
inserted flange fixed with solder.
Qualitative x-ray fluorescence
analysis identified the presence of
silver, copper, and zinc.

151. BEAKER WITH HUMAN FACE

Chimú style, North Coast, Peru
Silver alloy
43.2 × 13.3 × 13.9 cm
TL.2009.20.89
Composed of five separate sheet
sections soldered together. Qualitative x-ray fluorescence analysis
identified the presence of silver and
copper with traces of zinc and iron.

152. HUMAN EFFIGY FIGURE

Chimú style, North Coast, Peru
Hammered gold alloy sheet
26.7 × 7.6 × 7.8 cm
TL.2009.20.73
Qualitative x-ray fluorescence
analysis identified the presence of
gold, copper, and silver.

153. CEREMONIAL KNIFE BLADE

Chimú (?), Catacaos area,
North Coast, Peru
Late Intermediate, 1100–1450 CE
Copper alloy
10.7 × 15.3 × 0.3 cm
TL.2009.20.275

154. EFFIGY FIGURE

Inka style, Peru
Cast silver alloy
9 × 1.9 × 2.3 cm
TL.2009.20.243

155. EFFIGY FIGURE

Inka style, Peru
Cast silver alloy
7.5 × 2.2 × 2 cm
TL.2009.20.244

156. LLAMA

Inka, Peru
1400–1534 CE
Cast silver alloy
2.3 × 3.3 × 0.8 cm
TL.2009.20.245

157. LLAMA

Inka, Peru
1400–1534 CE
Cast silver alloy
5.8 × 5.4 × 1.3 cm
TL.2009.20.246

158. SHELL EFFIGY PECTORAL

Inka (?), northern Peru or Ecuador (?)
1400–1534 CE
Earthenware
6.35 × 18.29 × 8.89 cm
TL.2009.20.145

ABBREVIATED REFERENCES

Agurcia Fasquelle 2005. R. Agurcia Fasquelle. "Rosalila: Temple of the Sun King at Copan." In *Lords of Creation: The Origin of Sacred Maya Kingship*, exh. cat., Los Angeles County Museum of Art, ed. V. M. Fields and D. Reents-Budet, 72–73. Los Angeles and London: LAMCA and Scala.

Alderson 2002. S. Alderson. "A Technological Study of the Painted Surfaces of Zapotec Urns from Xoxocotlán." *American Institute for Conservation: Objects Specialty Group Postprints* 9:146–60.

Alva and Donnan 1993. W. Alva and C. Donnan. "Moche Warfare and the Sacrifice of Prisoners." In *Royal Tombs of Sipán*, exh. cat., Los Angeles: Fowler Museum of Cultural History, ed. W. Alva and C. Donnan, 127–41. Berkeley and Los Angeles: University of California Press.

Anawalt 1998. P. Riefe Anawalt. "They Came to Trade Exquisite Things: Ancient West Mexican-Ecuadorian Contacts." In *Ancient West Mexico: Art and Archaeology of the Unknown Past*, exh. cat., Art Institute of Chicago, ed. R. F. Townsend, 233–49. Chicago and New York: Art Institute of Chicago and Thames & Hudson.

Ancona-Ha, Pérez De Lara, and Van Stone 2000. P. Ancona-Ha, J. Pérez De Lara, and M. Van Stone. "Some Observations on Hand Gestures in Maya Art." In *The Maya Vase Book*, vol. 6, ed. B. Kerr and J. Kerr, 1072–89. New York: Kerr Associates.

Bassie 2002. K. Bassie. *Maya Creator Gods.* http://www.mesoweb.com/features/bassie/CreatorGods/CreatorGods.pdf

Boone 1978. E. H. Boone, ed. *Falsifications and Misrepresentations of Pre-Columbian Art*. Washington, DC: Dumbarton Oaks Research Library and Collection.

Boone 1985. E. H. Boone, ed. *Painted Architecture and Polychrome Monumental Sculpture in Mesoamerica.*

Washington, DC: Dumbarton Oaks Research Library and Collection.

Boone 1993. E. H. Boone, ed. *Collecting the Pre-Columbian Past*. Washington, DC: Dumbarton Oaks Research Library and Collection.

Boone 1996. E. H. Boone, ed. *Andean Art at Dumbarton Oaks*, vol 1. Washington, DC: Dumbarton Oaks Research Library and Collection.

Boston 1992. R. Stone-Miller, ed. *To Weave for the Sun: Andean Textiles in the Museum of Fine Arts Boston.* Exh. cat., Boston: Museum of Fine Arts. New York and London: Thames & Hudson.

Botero 2007. C. I. Botero, et al., *The Art of Gold: The Legacy of Pre-Hispanic Colombia. The Collection of the Gold Museum in Bogotá*. Bogotá and Milan: Skira.

Bradley 2001. D. E. Bradley. "Gender, Power, and Fertility in the Olmec Ritual Ballgame." In *The Sport of Life and Death: The Mesoamerican Ballgame*, exh. cat., Charlotte, NC: Mint Museum, ed. E. M. Worthington, 32–39. New York: Thames & Hudson.

Bray 1981. W. Bray. "Gold Work." In *Between Continents/Between Seas: Precolumbian Art of Costa Rica*, exh. cat., Detroit Institute of Arts, ed. S. Abel-Vidor et al., 154–56. New York: Abrams

Bray 1993. W. Bray. "Techniques of Gilding and Surface Enrichment in Pre-Hispanic American Metallurgy." In *Metal Plating and Patination: Cultural, Technical and Historical Developments*, ed. S. La Niece and P. Craddock, 182–92. Oxford: Butterworth-Heinemann.

Bray 2005. W. Bray. "Craftsmen and Farmers: The Archaeology of the Yotoco Period." In *Calima and Malagana: Art and Archaeology in Southwestern Colombia*, ed. M. Cardale Schrimpf , 106–10. Bogotá: Pro Calima Foundation.

Brent 2001. M. Brent. "The Limits of TL." *Archaeology* 54, no. 1 (January–February).

Bruhns and Kelker 2010. K. O. Bruhns and N. L. Kelker. *Faking the Ancient Andes*. Walnut Creek, CA: Left Coast Press.

Butterwick 1998. K. Butterwick. "Food for the Dead: The West Mexican Art of Feasting." In *Ancient West Mexico: Art and Archaeology of the Unknown Past*, exh. cat., Art Institute of Chicago, ed. R. F. Townsend, 89–106. Chicago and New York: Art Institute of Chicago and Thames & Hudson.

Byland and Pohl 1994. B. E. Byland and J. M. D. Pohl. *In the Realm of 8 Deer: The Archaeology of the Mixtec Codices*. Norman: University of Oklahoma Press.

Caso and Bernal 1952. A. Caso and I. Bernal. *Urnas de Oaxaca*. Memorias 2. Mexico City: Instituto Nacional de Antropología e Historia.

Chapdelaine, Kennedy, and Uceda Castillo 2001. C. Chapdelaine, G. Kennedy, and S. Uceda Castillo. "Neutron Activation Analysis of Metal Artifacts from the Moche Site, North Coast of Peru." *Archaeometry* 43, no. 3: 373–91.

Coe 1993. M. D. Coe. "From *Huaqhero* to Connoisseur: The Early Market in Pre-Columbian Art." In *Collecting the Pre-Columbian Past*, ed. E. H. Boone, 271–90. Washington, DC: Dumbarton Oaks Research Library and Collection.

Coe and Kerr 1998. M. D. Coe and J. Kerr. *The Art of the Maya Scribe*. New York: Abrams.

Colburn 2002. F. D. Colburn. *Latin America at the End of Politics*. Princeton: Princeton University Press.

Conklin 2004. W. J. Conklin. "Color and Abstraction in Wari Weaving." In *Tiwanaku: Ancestors of the Inca*, exh. cat., Denver Art Museum, ed. M. Young-Sánchez, 180–86.

Denver and Lincoln: Denver Art Museum and University of Nebraska Press.

Cordy-Collins 1996. A. Cordy-Collins. "Lambayeque." In *Andean Art at Dumbarton Oaks*, vol. 1, ed. E. H. Boone, 189–222. Washington, DC: Dumbarton Oaks Research Library and Collection.

Craddock 2009. P. Craddock. *Scientific Investigations of Copies, Fakes and Forgeries*. London: Archetype.

Denver 2004. M. Young-Sánchez, ed. *Tiwanaku: Ancestors of the Inca*. Exh. cat., Denver Art Museum. Denver and Lincoln: Denver Art Museum and University of Nebraska Press.

Detroit 1981. S. Abel-Vidor, et al. *Between Continents/ Between Seas: Precolumbian Art of Costa Rica*. Exh. cat., Detroit Institute of Arts. Detroit and New York: Detroit Institute of Arts and Abrams.

Donnan and McClelland 1999. C. Donnan and D. Mc-Clelland. *Moche Fineline Painting: Its Evolution and Its Artists*. Los Angeles: UCLA Fowler Museum of Cultural History.

Emmerich 1965. A. Emmerich. *Sweat of the Sun and Tears of the Moon: Gold and Silver in Pre-Columbian Art*. Seattle: University of Washington Press; repr. New York: Hacker Art Books, 1977 and 1984.

Emmerich and Lothrop 1954. A. Emmerich and S. K. Lothrop. "A Peruvian Goldsmith's Grave." *Archaeology* 7, no. 1: 31–36.

Fash 1991. W. Fash, *Scribes, Warriors, and Kings: The City of Copán and the Ancient Maya*. New York and London: Thames & Hudson.

Felleman 1982. S. Felleman. Introduction. In *Pre-Columbian Art of Ecuador from the Peggy and Tessim Zorach Collection*, exh. cat., Ithaca, NY: Herbert E. Johnson Museum of Art, 7–13. Ithaca, NY: Cornell University Press.

Fields 1989. V. M. Fields. "The Origins of Divine Kingship among the Lowland Classic Maya." Ph.D. diss., University of Texas at Austin.

Fields 1991. V. M. Fields. "The Iconographic Heritage of the Maya Jester God." In *Sixth Palenque Round Table*, ed. M. G. Robertson and V. M. Fields, 167–74. Norman: University of Oklahoma Press.

Fields and Reents-Budet 2005. V. M. Fields and D. Reents-Budet. "Introduction: The First Sacred Kings of Mesoamerica." In *Lords of Creation: The Origin of Sacred Maya Kingship*, exh. cat., Los Angeles County Museum of Art, ed. V. M. Fields and D. Reents-Budet, 21–27. Los Angeles and London: LACMA and Scala.

Fleming 1992. S. Fleming. "Appendices A and B: Sitio Conte Goldworking Techniques: Hammering and Casting, and Alloying and the Treatment of Surfaces." In *River of Gold: Precolumbian Treasures from Sitio Conte*, ed. P. Hearne and R. J. Sharer, 48–58. Philadelphia: The University Museum of Archaeology and Anthropology, University of Pennsylvania.

Fletcher 2002. J. M. Fletcher. "Stuccoed Tripod Vessels from Teotihuacan: An Examination of Materials and Manufacture." *Journal of the American Institute for Conservation* 41, no. 2 (Summer 2002): 139–54.

Fort Worth 1986. L. Schele and M. E. Miller, eds. *The Blood of Kings: Dynasty and Ritual in Maya Art*. Exh. cat., Fort Worth: Kimbell Art Museum. New York and London: George Brazillier and Thames & Hudson.

Freidel, Schele, and Parker 1993. D. Freidel, L. Schele, and J. Parker. *Maya Cosmos: Three Thousand Years on the Shaman's Path*. New York: W. Morrow, 1993.

Furst 1998. P. T. Furst. "Shamanic Symbolism, Transformation, and Deities in West Mexican Funerary Art." In *Ancient West Mexico: Art and Archaeology of the Un-*

known Past, exh. cat., Art Institute of Chicago, ed. R. F. Townsend, 169–89. Chicago and New York: Art Institute of Chicago and Thames & Hudson

Goldstein 1988. M. M. Goldstein. "Veracruz and the Development of Mesoamerican Civilization." In *Ceremonial Sculpture of Ancient Veracruz*, exh. cat., Brookville, NY: Hillwood Art Gallery, Long Island University, ed. M. M. Goldstein, 169–89. Brookville, NY: Hillwood Art Gallery.

Goodall 2008. R. A. Goodall. "Micro-Attenuated Total Reflection Spectral Imaging in Archaeology: Application to Maya Paint and Plaster Wall Decorations." *Applied Spectroscopy* 62, no. 1: 10–16.

Gorelick and Gwinnett 1994. L. Gorelick and A. J. Gwinnett. "Beads from Sipán: A Functional Analysis." In *Archaeometry of Pre-Columbian Sites and Artifacts: Proceedings of a Symposium Organized by the UCLA Institute of Archaeology and the Getty Conservation Institute, Los Angeles, California, March 23–27, 1992*, ed. D. A. Scott and P. Meyers, 175–80. Los Angeles: Getty Conservation Institute.

Graham 1998. M. M. Graham. "The Iconography of Rulership in Ancient West Mexico." In *Ancient West Mexico: Art and Archaeology of the Unknown Past*, exh. cat., Art Institute of Chicago, ed. R. F. Townsend, 191–203. Chicago and New York: Art Institute of Chicago and Thames & Hudson.

Griffin 1972. G. G. Griffin. "Xochipala, the Earliest Great Art Style in Mexico." *Proceedings of the American Philosophical Society* 116, no. 4: 301–9.

Grube and Nahm 1994. N. Grube and W. Nahm. "A Concensus of Xibalba: A Complete Inventory of 'Way' Characters on Maya Ceramics." In *The Maya Vase Book*, vol. 4, ed. B. Kerr and J. Kerr, 686–715. New York: Kerr Associates.

Guenter 2007. S. Guenter. "The Tomb of K'inich Janaab Pakal: The Temple of the Inscriptions at Palenque." *Mesoweb* (2007): www.mesoweb.com/articles/guenter/TI.pdf.

Gwinnett and Gorelick 1979. A. J. Gwinnett and L. Gorelick. "Ancient Lapidary: A Study Using Scanning Electron Microscopy and Functional Analysis." *Expedition* 22, no. 1: 17–32.

Harrison and Beaubien 2010. A. Harrison and H. F. Beaubien. "Bringing Context to the Smithsonian Collections of Pre-Columbian Gold from Panama through Technical Examination and Analysis." In *Metal 2010: Proceedings of the Interim Meeting of the ICOM-CC Metal Working Group, October 11–15, 2010, Charleston, South Carolina, USA,* 198–203. Charleston: Clemson University.

Hearn 2008. K. Hearn. "Ancient Iron Ore Mine Discovered in Peruvian Andes." *National Geographic News,* written February 11, 2008, published online October 28, 2008, accessed 2/23/2011, http://news.nationalgeographic.com/news/2008/02/080211-nasca-mine.html.

Heyden 1971. D. Heyden. "A New Interpretation of the Smiling Figures." In *Ancient Art of Veracruz,* exh. cat., Los Angeles County Museum of Natural History, ed. O. Hammer. Los Angeles: Ethnic Arts Council.

Heyden 1981. D. Heyden. "Caves, Gods, and Myths: World-View and Planning in Teotihuacan." In *Mesoamerican Sites and World-Views: Proceedings of a Conference at Dumbarton Oaks, October 16–17, 1976,* ed. E. Benson, 1–35. Washington, DC: Dumbarton Oaks Research Library and Collection.

Hill 1999. W. D. Hill. "Ballcourts, Competitive Games, and the Emergence of Complex Society." Ph.D. diss., University of British Columbia, Vancouver.

Hörz and Kallfass 1998. G. Hörz and M. Kallfass. "Pre-Colombian Metalworking in Peru: Ornamental and Ceremonial Objects from the Royal Tombs of Sipán." *Journal of the Mineral: Metals and Materials Research Society* 50, no. 12: 8–16.

Houston et al. 2009. S. Houston, C. Brittenham, C. Mesick, A. Tokovinine, and C. Warriner. *Veiled Brightness: A History of Ancient Maya Color.* Austin: University of Texas Press.

Houston, Robertson, and Stuart 2001. S. Houston, J. Robertson, and D. Stuart. *Quality and Quantity in Glyphic Nouns and Adjectives.* Research Reports on Ancient Maya Writing 47. Washington, DC: Center for Maya Research.

Howe 1985. E. Howe. "A Radiographic Study of Some Hollow-Cast Gold Pendants from Sitio Conte." In *Pre-Columbian Metallurgy: Forty-Fifth International Congress of Americanists,* 189–200. Bogotá: Banco de la Republica.

Indianapolis 1988. L. A. Parsons, J. B. Carlson, and P. D. Joralemon. *The Face of Ancient America: The Wally and Brenda Zollman Collection of Precolumbian Art.* Exh. cat., Indianapolis Museum of Art. Indianapolis: Indiana University Press.

Ithaca 1982. *Pre-Columbian Art of Ecuador from the Peggy and Tessim Zorach Collection.* Exh. cat., Ithaca, NY: Herbert F. Johnson Museum of Art, Cornell University. Ithaca: Herbert Johnson Museum of Art.

Jackson 2007. E. Jackson. "Gold Alloys from pre-Columbian Panama: New Discoveries." *Panama News* 13, no. 15 (August 6–18).

Jímenez Moreno 1972. W. Jímenez Moreno. "Estratigrafia y tipología religiosas." In *Religión en Mesoamérica,* ed. J. L. King and N. Castillo Tejero, 31–36. Puebla, Mexico: Sociedad Mexicana de Antropología.

Joralemon 1974. P. D. Joralemon. "The Olmec Dragon: A Study in Pre-Columbian Iconography." In *Origins of Religious Art and Iconography in Preclassic Mesoamerica,* ed. H. B. Nicholson, 27–71. Los Angeles: UCLA Latin American Center.

José-Yacaman et al. 1996. M. José-Yacaman, L. Rendón, J. Arenas, and M. C. Serra Puche. "Maya Blue Paint: An Ancient Nanostructured Material." *Science* 273, no. 5272: 223–25.

Kan 1970. M. Kan. "The Pre-Columbian Art of West Mexico: Nayarit, Jalisco and Colima." In *Sculpture of Ancient West Mexico: Nayarit, Jalisco, Colima,* exh. cat., Los Angeles County Museum of Art, ed. M. Kan, C. Meighan, and H. B. Nicholson, 13–27. Los Angeles and Albuquerque: LACMA and University of New Mexico Press.

Kelly 1949. I. Kelly. *The Archaeology of the Autlan-Tuscacuesco Area of Jalisco,* vol. 2, *The Tuscacuesco-Zapotitlan Zone,* Ibero-Americana 27. Berkeley: University of California Press.

Kelly 1974. I. Kelly. "Stirrup Pots from Colima." In *The Archaeology of West Mexico,* ed. B. Bell, 206–11. Ajijic, Jalisco: West Mexican Society for Advanced Study.

Kolata 2004. A. Kolata. "The Flow of Cosmic Power: Religion, Ritual, and the People of Tiwanaku." In *Tiwanaku: Ancestors of the Inca,* exh. cat., Denver Art Museum ed. M. Young-Sánchez, 96–125. Denver and Lincoln: University of Nebraska Press.

Labbé 1992. A. Labbé, *Images of Power: Masterworks of the Bowers Museum of Cultural Art.* Santa Ana, CA: Bowers Museum of Cultural Art and Cultural Arts Press.

Labbé 1995. A. Labbé. *Guardians of the Life Stream: Shamans, Art and Power in Prehispanic Central Panamá.* Santa Ana, CA: Bowers Museum of Cultural Art and Cultural Arts Press.

Lange 1993. F. Lange, ed. *Pre-Columbian Jade: New Geological and Cultural Interpretations.* Salt Lake City: University of Utah Press.

Lechtman 1971. H. Lechtman. "Ancient Methods of Gilding Silver: Examples from the Old and New World." In *Science and Archaeology* 4: *Symposium on Archaeological Chemistry, Held in Atlantic City, N.J., on September 9–11, 1968,* ed. R. H. Brill, 20–30. Cambridge, MA and London: MIT Press.

Lechtman 1973. H. Lechtman. "A Tumbaga Object from the High Andes of Venezuela." *American Antiquity* 38, no. 4: 473–82.

Lechtman 1980. H. Lechtman. "The Central Andes: Metallurgy without Iron." In *The Coming Age of Iron,* ed. T. A. Wertime and J. D. Muhly, 267–334. New Haven: Yale University Press.

Lechtman 1985. H. Lechtman. "The Significance of Metals in Pre-Columbian Andean Culture." *Bulletin of the American Academy of Arts and Sciences* 38 (5): 9–37.

Lechtman 1996a. H. Lechtman. "Technical Description of Fourteen Feline Faces." In *Andean Art at Dumbarton Oaks,* vol. 1, ed. E. H. Boone, 261. Washington, DC: Dumbarton Oaks Research Library and Collection.

Lechtman 1996b. H. Lechtman, "Technical Description of a Lambayeque Silver Disk." In *Andean Art at Dumbarton*

Oaks, vol. 1, ed. E. H. Boone, 220–22. Washington, DC: Dumbarton Oaks Research Library and Collection.

Lechtman, Erlij, and Barry 1982. H. Lechtman, A. Erlij, and E. J. Barry Jr. "New Perspectives on Moche Metallurgy: Techniques of Gilding Copper at Loma Negra, Northern Peru." *American Antiquity* 47, no. 1: 473–82.

Leona et al. 2004. M. Leona et al. "Identification of the Pre-Columbian Pigment Maya Blue on Works of Art by Noninvasive UV-Vis and Raman Spectroscopic Techniques." *Journal of the American Institute for Conservation* 43, no. 1: 39–54.

Looper, Reents-Budet, and Bishop 2009. M. Looper, D. Reents-Budet, and R. L. Bishop. "Dance on Classic Maya Ceramics." In *To Be Like Gods: Dance in Ancient Maya Civilization,* ed. M. Looper, 113–50. Austin: University of Texas Press.

Los Angeles 1970. M. Kan, C. Meighan, and H. B. Nicholson, eds. *Sculpture of Ancient West Mexico: Nayarit, Jalisco, Colima: A Catalog of the Proctor Stafford Collection at the Los Angeles County Museum of Art.* Exh. cat., Los Angeles County Museum of Art. Los Angeles and Albuquerque: LACMA and University of New Mexico Press.

Los Angeles 1972. H. von Winning and O. Hammer. *Anecdotal Sculpture of Ancient West Mexico.* Exh. cat., Los Angeles: Natural History Museum. Los Angeles: Ethnic Arts Council of Los Angeles.

Los Angeles 1976. C. Donnan, ed. *Moche Art of Peru: Pre-Columbian Symbolic Communication.* Exh. cat., Los Angeles: Museum of Cultural History, University of California.

Los Angeles 1993. W. Alva and C. Donnan, eds. *Royal Tombs of Sipán.* Exh. cat., Los Angeles: Fowler Museum of Cultural History.

Los Angeles 2005. V. M. Fields and D. Reents-Budet, eds. *Lords of Creation: The Origin of Sacred Maya Kingship.* Exh. cat., Los Angeles County Museum of Art. Los Angeles and London: LACMA and Scala.

Markman and Markman 1989. R. H. Markman and P. T. Markman, *Masks of the Spirit: Image and Metaphor in Mesoamerica.* Berkeley: University of California Press.

Martin 2007. S. Martin. "Cacao in Ancient Maya Religion." In *Chocolate in Mesoamerica: A Cultural History of Cacao,* ed. C. L. McNeil, 154–83. Gainesville: University Press of Florida.

Matos Moctezuma 1984. E. Matos Moctezuma. "The Templo Mayor of Tenochtitlán: Economics and Ideology." In *Ritual Human Sacrifice in Mesoamerica,* ed. E. H. Boone, 133–64. Washington, DC: Dumbarton Oaks Research Library and Collection.

McBride 1971. H. W. McBride. "Figurine Types of Central and Southern Veracruz." In *Ancient Art of Veracruz,* exh. cat., Los Angeles County Museum of Natural History, ed. O. Hammer, 23–30. Los Angeles: Ethnic Arts Council.

Medellín Zenil and Peterson 1954. A. Medellín Zenil and F. A. Peterson. "A Smiling Head Complex from Central Veracruz, Mexico." *American Antiquity* 20, no. 2: 162–69.

Meighan and Nicholson 1970. C. Meighan and H. B. Nicholson. "The Ceramic Mortuary Offerings of Prehistorical West Mexico: An Archaeological Perspective." In *Sculpture of Ancient West Mexico: Nayarit, Jalisco, Colima,* exh. cat., Los Angeles County Museum of Art, ed. M. Kan, C. Meighan, and H. B. Nicholson, 29–69. Los Angeles and Albuquerque: LACMA and University of New Mexico Press.

M. Miller and Taube 1993. M. Miller and K. Taube. *The Gods and Symbols of Ancient Mexico and the Maya: An Illustrated Dictionary of Mesoamerican Religion.* New York: Thames & Hudson.

V. E. Miller 1981. V. E. Miller. "Pose and Gesture in Classic Maya Monumental Sculpture." Ph.D. diss., University of Texas, Austin.

Monaghan 1990. J. Monaghan. "Reciprocity, Redistribution, and the Transaction of Value in the Mesoamerican Fiesta." *American Ethnologist* 17: 758–74.

Moseley 2001. M. E. Moseley. *The Incas and Their Ancestors: The Archaeology of Peru.* Rev. ed. New York and London: Thames & Hudson.

New York 1970. E. K. Easby and J. F. Scott, eds. *Before Cortés: Sculpture of Middle America.* Exh. cat., New York: The Metropolitan Museum of Art. New York Graphic Society.

New York 1970. H. King, P. Carcedo de Mufarech, and L. J. Castillo, eds. *Rain of the Moon: Silver in Ancient Peru.* Exh. cat., New York: The Metropolitan Museum of Art. New Haven: Yale University Press.

New York 1970. F. R. Solís Olguín, ed. *The Aztec Empire.* Exh. cat., New York: Solomon R. Guggenheim Museum.

Nicholson 1971. H. B. Nicholson. "The Iconography of Central Veracruz Ceramic Sculptures." In *Ancient Art of Veracruz,* exh. cat., Los Angeles County Museum of Natural History, ed. O. Hammer. Los Angeles: Ethnic Arts Council.

O'Grady 2005. C. O'Grady. "Morphological and Chemical Analyses of Manganese Oxide Accretions on Mexican Ceramics." In *Materials Issues in Art and Archaeology 7,* ed. P. B. Vandiver et al., 182–92. Warrendale, PA: Materials Research Society.

Olsen 2002. D. A. Olsen. *Music of El Dorado: The Ethnomusicology of Ancient South American Cultures.* Gainesville: University Press of Florida.

Pasztory 1983. E. Pasztory. *Aztec Art.* New York: Abrams.

Pasztory 2002. E. Pasztory. "Truth in Forgery: The Western Concept of Pre-Columbian Art." *West by Nonwest,* special issue of *RES: Anthropology and Aesthetics* 42:159–65.

Pickering and Cabrero 1998. R. B. Pickering and M. T. Cabrero. "Mortuary Practices in the Shaft-Tomb Region." In *Ancient West Mexico: Art and Archaeology of the Unknown Past,* exh. cat., Art Institute of Chicago, ed. R. F. Townsend, 71–91. Chicago and New York: Art Institute of Chicago and Thames & Hudson.

Piña Chan 1968. Román Piña Chan. *Jaina: La casa en el agua.* Mexico City: Instituto Nacional de Antropología.

Princeton 1995. M. D. Coe et al. *The Olmec World: Ritual and Rulership.* Exh. cat., Princeton University Art Museum. New York: Abrams.

Proulx 2006. D. A. Proulx. *A Sourcebook of Nasca Ceramic Iconography: Reading a Culture through its Art.* Iowa City: University of Iowa Press.

Reents-Budet 2000. D. Reents-Budet. "Feasting among the Classic Maya: Evidence from Pictorial Ceramics." In *The Maya Vase Book,* vol. 6, ed. B. Kerr and J. Kerr, 1022–38. New York: Kerr Associates.

Reents-Budet 2005. D. Reents-Budet. "Mesoamerica." In *Masters of the Americas: In Praise of the Pre-Columbian Artists. The Dora and Paul Janssen Collection,* exh. cat.,

Geneva: Musées d'art et d'histoire, ed. G. Le Fort, 48–93. Brussels and Milan: 5 Continents Editions.

Reents-Budet 2009. D. Reents-Budet. "The Transformed Self: Performance Masks of Mexico." In D. Reents-Budet, *Passionate Journey: The Gretchen and Nelson Grice Collection of Native American Art*, exh. cat., Charlotte, NC: The Mint Museum, 55–91.

Reilly 1995. F. Kent Reilly III. "Art, Ritual, and Rulership in the Olmec World." In *The Olmec World: Ritual and Rulership*, exh. cat., Princeton University Art Museum, ed. M. D. Coe et al., 27–45. New York: Abrams.

Reilly and Tate 1995. F. Kent Reilly III and C. Tate. "Contortion and Transformation." In *The Olmec World: Ritual and Rulership*, exh. cat., Princeton University Art Museum, ed. M. D. Coe et al., 166–72. New York: Abrams.

Roundhill et al. 1989. L. Roundhill et al. "Maya Blue: A Fresh Look at an Old Controversy." In *Seventh Palenque Round Table, 1989*, ed. M. Greene Robertson and V. M. Fields, 253–56. San Francisco: Pre-Columbian Art Research Institute.

Rovira 1994. S. Rovira. "Pre-Hispanic Goldwork from the Museo de América, Madrid: A New Set of Analyses." In *Archaeometry of Pre-Columbian Sites and Artifacts*, ed. D. A. Scott and P. Meyers, 323–50. Los Angeles: Getty Conservation Institute.

San Francisco 2010. K. Berrin and V. M. Fields, eds. *Olmec: Colossal Masterworks of Ancient Mexico*. Exh. cat., San Francisco: Fine Arts Museums of San Francisco. New Haven: Yale University Press.

Sax et al. 2008. M. Sax, J. M. Walsh, I. C. Freestone, A. H. Rankin, and N. D. Meeks. "The Origins of Two Purportedly Pre-Columbian Mexican Crystal Skulls." *Journal of Archaeological Science* 35:2751–60.

Scarborough and Wilcox 1991. V. Scarborough and D. Wilcox. *The Mesoamerican Ballgame*. Tucson: University of Arizona Press.

Schele 1997. L. Schele, *Hidden Faces of the Maya*. Poway, CA: Alti.

Schorsch 1998. D. Schorsch. "Silver-and-Gold Moche Artifacts from Loma Negra, Peru." *Metropolitan Museum Journal* 33:109–36.

D. Scott 1980. D. A. Scott. "The Conservation and Analysis of Some Ancient Copper Alloy Beads from Colombia." *Studies in Conservation* 25: 157–64.

D. Scott 1986. D. A. Scott. "Gold and Silver Alloys Coatings over Copper." *Archaeometry* 28, no. 1: 33–50.

D. Scott 1991a. D. A. Scott. "Examination of Some Gold Wire from Pre-Hispanic South America." *Studies in Conservation* 36, no. 2: 65–75.

D. Scott 1991b. D. A. Scott. *Metallography and Microstructure of Ancient and Historic Metals*. Los Angeles: Getty Conservation Institute.

D. Scott 1994. D. A. Scott. "Goldwork of Pre-Columbian Costa Rica and Panama: A Technical Study." In *Material Issues in Art and Archaeology* 4, ed. P. Vandiver, J. Druzik, and I. Freestone, 499–526. Pittsburgh: Materials Research Society.

D. Scott 2000. D. A. Scott. "A Review of Gilding Techniques in Ancient South America." In *Gilded Metals: History, Technology and Conservation,* ed. T. Drayman-Weisser, 203–22. London: Archetype Publications.

D. Scott and Bray 1980. D. A. Scott and W. Bray. "Ancient Platinum Technology in South America: Its Use by the Indians in pre-Hispanic Times." *Platinum Metals Review* (1980): 24 (4): 147–57.

J. Scott 2001. J. F. Scott. "Dressed to Kill: Stone Regalia of the Mesoamerican Ballgame." In *The Sport of Life and Death: The Mesoamerican Ballgame,* exh. cat., Charlotte, NC: The Mint Museum, ed. E. M. Worthington, 50–63. New York: Thames & Hudson.

Sellen 2003. A. T. Sellen. "Corn as Blood and Blood as Seed." In *Reframing Zapotec Religion*, ed. J. Urcid and D. Tavárez. Waltham, MA.

Shaplin 1978. P. D. Shaplin. "Thermoluminescence and Style in Authentication of Ceramic Sculpture from Oaxaca, Mexico." *Archaeometry* 20, no. 1: 47–54.

Shimada, Griffin, and Gordus 2000. I. Shimada, J. A. Griffin, and A. Gordus. "The Technology, Iconography and Social Significance of Metals: A Multi-Dimensional Analysis of Middle Sican Objects." In *Pre-Columbian Gold: Technology, Style, and Iconography,* ed. C. McEwan, 28–61. London: Fitzroy Dearborn Publishers.

Stevenson Day 1988. J. Stevenson Day. "The West Mexican Ballgame." In *Ancient West Mexico: Art and Archaeology of the Unknown Past*, exh. cat., Art Institute of Chicago, ed. R. F. Townsend, 151–67. Chicago and New York: Art Institute of Chicago and Thames & Hudson.

Stirling and Stirling 1942. M. Stirling and M. Stirling. "Finding Jewels of Jade in the Mexican Swamp." *National Geographic* 82:635–61.

Stone-Miller 2002a. R. Stone-Miller. *Art of the Andes from Chavín to Inca*. London: Thames & Hudson.

Stone-Miller 2002b. R. Stone-Miller. *Seeing with New Eyes: Highlights of the Michael C. Carlos Collection of Art of the Ancient Americas*. Atlanta: Michael C. Carlos Museum.

Strahan and Fenn 2007. D. Strahan and M. Fenn. "A Transfer of Technology: Jade Abrasive Methods Used to Create Inscriptions in Ancient Chinese Bronzes." In *Scientific Research on the Sculptural Arts of Asia: Proceedings of the Third Forbes Symposium at the Freer Gallery of Art*, ed. J. G. Douglas, P. Jett, and J. Winter, 26–36. London: Archetype.

Stuart 1996. D. Stuart. "Kings of Stone: A Consideration of Stelae in Ancient Maya Ritual and Representation." *RES: Anthropology and Aesthetics* 29/30:148–71.

Stuart 2007. D. Stuart. "The Language of Chocolate: References to Cacao on Classic Maya Drinking Vessels." In *Chocolate in Mesoamerica: A Cultural History of Cacao*, ed. C. L. McNeil, 184–201. Gainesville: University Press of Florida.

Sullivan 1986. L. E. Sullivan. "Sound and Senses: Toward a Hermeneutics of Performance." *History of Religions* 26, no. 1: 15–33.

Tate 1995. C. Tate. "Art in Olmec Culture." In *The Olmec World: Ritual and Rulership*, exh. cat., Princeton University Art Museum, ed. M. D. Coe et al., 47–67. New York: Abrams.

Taube 2005. K. A. Taube. "The Rainmakers: The Olmec and Their Contribution to Mesoamerican Belief and Ritual." In *Lords of Creation: The Origin of Sacred Maya Kingship*, exh. cat., Los Angeles County Museum of Art, ed. V. M. Fields and D. Reents-Budet, 21–27. London and Los Angeles: Scala.

Thompson 1970. J. E. Thompson, *Maya History and Religion*. Norman: University of Oklahoma Press.

Toscano 1946. S. Toscano. "El arte y la historia del occidente en México." In *Arte precolombino del occidente de México*, ed. S. Toscano, P. Kirchoff, and D. F. Rubín de Borbolla, 9–33. Mexico City: Dirección General de Educación Extra-Escolar y Estética.

Townsend 1998a. R. F. Townsend. "Introduction: Renewing the Inquiry in Ancient West Mexico." In *Ancient West Mexico: Art and Archaeology of the Unknown Past*, exh. cat., Art Institute of Chicago, ed. R. F. Townsend, 15–33. Chicago and New York: Art Institute of Chicago and Thames & Hudson.

Townsend 1998b. R. F. Townsend. "Before Gods, Before Kings." In *Ancient West Mexico: Art and Archaeology of the Unknown Past*, exh. cat., Art Institute of Chicago, ed. R. F. Townsend, 107–35. Chicago and New York: Art Institute of Chicago and Thames & Hudson.

Urcid 2005. J. Urcid. *Zapotec Writing: Knowledge, Power, and Memory in Ancient Oaxaca*. Waltham, MA: FAMSI.

Vandenabeele et al. 2005. P. Vandenabeele et al. "Raman Spectroscopic Analysis of the Maya Wall Paintings in Ek'Balam, Mexico." *Spectrochimica Acta, Part A 65* (2005):2349–56.

Von Winning 1974. H. von Winning. *The Shaft Tomb Figures of West Mexico*. Southwest Museum Papers 24. Los Angeles: Southwest Museum.

Walsh 2005. J. M. Walsh. "What is Real? A New Look at Pre-Columbian Mesoamerican Collections." *AnthroNotes* 26, no. 1: 3–19.

Washington 1996. E. Benson and B. de la Fuente, eds. *Olmec Art of Ancient Mexico*. Exh.. cat., Washington, DC: National Gallery of Art.

West 1963. E. West. "Jade: Its Character and Occurrence." *Expedition* 5, no. 2: 3–10.

Wilkerson 2010. J. Wilkerson. "Art of the Gulf Coast Lowlands: The Classic Veracruz Florescence and Postclassic Huastec Apogee." In *Ancient Mexican Art at Dumbarton Oaks: Central Highlands, Southwestern Highlands, Gulf Lowlands*, ed. S. Evans. Washington, DC: Dumbarton Oaks Research Library and Collection.

ACKNOWLEDGMENTS

Among the many colleagues whose influence and inspiration underlie my contributions to this publication is Dr. Virginia Fields (1952–2011). Being the best of friends, college roommate, matron of honor, research collaborator, and co-curator of two nationally touring exhibitions, Ginny has profoundly molded my intellectual and professional approaches to the analysis and presentation of the art and culture history of the ancient Americas. Of particular importance for this project has been her generous sharing of curatorial and scientific analytical data, as well as long conversations, pertinent to the recognition of patterns of restoration and re-creations of West Mexican and Olmec objects. Her friendship and counsel are sorely missed.

The camaraderie of Juli and George Alderman has made this project all the more engaging, enlivened by animated conversations and a shared love of the ancient arts of Mexico. And to my husband, Ricardo, go my lasting thanks for his patience and endurance of hectic schedules, myriad travels, always-pending deadlines, and computer conundrums.   *Dorie Reents-Budet*

Many people generously offered their time and expertise toward the technical study of objects in the Bourne Collection. I thank Catherine Matsen, associate scientist and adjunct assistant professor at the University of Delaware for conducting Raman analysis, Barry Daly (MD, FRCR, professor of radiology, chief of abdominal imaging, and vice chair for research in the department of diagnostic radiology) and his staff at the University of Maryland Medical Center for donating their time, equipment, and expertise for the CT scanning of ceramics; Lynne A. Grant, chief conservator, University of Pennsylvania Museum of Archaeology and Anthropology, for access to the collections at the University Museum, Ellen Howe, Pamela Hatchfield, Virginia Fields, and Maureen Russell, for their participation and input during the West Mexican Ceramics Symposium Scholars Day. Richard Newman, head of scientific research at the Museum of Fine Arts, Boston, for his SEM analysis of metallographic cross sections; Lisha Glinsman, conservation scientist at the National Gallery of Art for the use of tumbaga alloy standards; and David Scott, professor of art history and archaeology and chair of the UCLA/Getty Program in Archaeological and Ethnographic Conservation, for his technical input.

The expertise and dedication of Walters conservation scientist Glenn Gates have added immeasurably to the art of the ancient Americas project. Thanks also go to Brianna Feston, conservation intern, New York University, for her work on objects in the collection; Stephanie Goldberg, conservation coordinator, for her assistance throughout the project and for her artistic contributions; Terry Drayman-Weisser and Meg Craft for their support, encouragement and insights throughout the project. And thanks especially to Jessica Arista for her contribution and enthusiasm for the project.   *Julie Lauffenburger*

INDEX

Italic numerals denote illustrations.

ILLUSTRATION CREDITS

Photographs and illustrations by the Walters Art Museum (Susan Tobin, photographer;
Stephanie Goldberg, illustrator) with the exception of the following:

Courtesy John Bourne: pp. vi, 1–22, 103
Carnegie Institution for Science, Washington, DC: p. 15 (top right)
Illustration by Stephanie Goldberg after Elizabeth K. Easby: p. 192, fig. 9
Heather Hurst and Leonard Ashby, Bonampak Documentation Project: p. 17
Justin Kerr, Kerr Associates, New York; pp. 42–43, 114, 116–17, 118
Digital Image © 2011 Museum Associates / LACMA / Art Resource, NY: p. 105
© Kate Russell Photography, Santa Fe, New Mexico: p. vii
University of Maryland Medical Center, Baltimore, Department of Radiology: p. 66
University of Pennsylvania Museum of Archaeology and Anthropology,
    Philadelphia: p. 191, fig. 7; 193 fig. 10A